BALA BHAGAVATAM

BY
SWAMI CHINMAYANANDA
AND
KUMARI BHARATHI NAIK

श्रृण्वन्तु सर्वे अमृतस्य पुत्रा :

Listen Ye! Children of Immortal Bliss!!

CENTRAL CHINMAYA MISSION TRUST

First Edition 1990 5000 copies
Reprint 1992 to August 2013 47,000 copies
Reprint November 2014 5,000 copies
Reprint June 2016 5,000 copies

Published by:
Chinmaya Prakashan
The Publications Division of
Central Chinmaya Mission Trust
Sandeepany Sadhanalaya
Saki Vihar Road, Mumbai 400072, India
Tel.: +91-22-2857 2367, 2857 5806 Fax: +91-22-2857 3065
Email: ccmtpublications@chinmayamission.com
Website: www.chinmayamission.com

Distribution Centre in USA:
Chinmaya Mission West
Publications Division
560 Bridgetown Pike
Langhorne, PA 19053, USA
Tel.: 1-888-CMW-READ, (215) 396-0390
Fax: (215) 396-9710
Email: publications@chinmayamission.org
Website: www.chinmayapublications.org

Printed by :
PRIYA GRAPHICS
Unit No. J - 120, Ansa Industrial Estate,
Saki Vihar Road, Sakinaka, (Andheri)
Mumbai - 400 072. Tel. No. 6695 9935, 4005 9936
Email: chinmayapriya@hotmail.com

Price : Rs : 115=00

ISBN: 978-81-7597-101-1

CONTENTS

PART I

PART II

CONTENTS—(Contd.)

ILLUSTRATIONS

LISTEN

The entire art and literature of India is moulded in the beauty and divinity of Bhagavat. From childhood onwards the Hindu heart is taught to beat in unison with the tenth-chapter here, which narrates the childhood stories of Lord Krishna. He is the one solitary symbol that generated and sustained the spiritual ideal in the heart of the children and appealed to the head of the elders.

The learned and the erudite revelled in the depth of the philosophy, packed away in all the serious "discussions" and "talks" that happen all along this glorious work of Vyasa. * However, the devoted young hearts of the children loved the stories of Krishna's early child-hood, full of pranks and mischiefs, meaningful adventures, and, purposeful jokes. He soon throws, upon the growing children, a divine light of blue-and-yellow, and all their life they grow to be fascinated with this ideal.

The ever-smiling, never-weeping, Krishna should be the ideal for the modern world of children everywhere, growing as they are, in a horrid atmosphere of fear, passions, and suspicions. The child, who has been nurtured, in his early days, upon these stories, cannot easily and readily be victimised by the confusions of the age around us. It is our duty, as parents, to give our children the blessings of this healthy orientation, both for their head and for their heart.

Whenever possible we have quoted from original Bhagavatam some selected portions of nice prayers with meanings. Encourage the children to repeat at least some of them.

These stories of Bala-Bhagavatam are to be read out by the *parents themselves* to their children. This must be done in an atmosphere of religious inspiration. Even if we are not able to arrange a complete 'Altar', at least let us keep a picture of Baby-Krishna on a table nearby, and let us decorate it with flowers, and light up a Joss-stick (Agarbathi) in humble reverence and devoted respect to the Lord.

Sit down, and let father (or mother) read out daily .... only *one section* a day. Repeat 10 times OM NAMO BHAGAVATE VASUDEVAYA.........and let the children repeat it in chorus. Let the portion read be translated in simple, homely words in the vernacular. *Tell* the story of Lord Krishna: never try to *teach* the stories to the children: NEVER, please.

At the end of the reading, the parents must prostrate before Lord Krishna's picture......please *never tell* your children to do so. Leave it for them to decide for themselves. Even those who were not doing it earlier, will start doing it now, of their own accord, voluntarily !

See that every following day, even the smallest baby in the group of listeners, can repeat the story narrated the previous day and the day before. Then only proceed ahead. See that the children remember the names of places, Rishis, people, etc. This is a subtle training both for improving their memory-power and for developing their powers of expressive narration. One by one all must tell the story to the others; others must correct the details.

We had earlier brought out the BALA RAMAYANA, and now in the preparation of this volume also, Miss Bharathi Naik had worked like a bull and lived like a hermit. I cannot thank her sufficiently. The sketches were also drawn by Miss Naik herself. She is not an artist; she had not trained herself for preparing sketches. She has drawn these *with* her love-for-Bala-vihar-children.

The Chinmaya Publication Trust could not take up the publication of this volume within such a short-time of one month. I was anxious that the volume must be ready for my children by the Yagna-time in November. So Tapovan Kuti undertook to publish the same. The Chinmaya Mission workers of Jamshedpur had worked in supreme dedication to make the volume so attractive. I am extremely indebted to every one of them.

Jai Jai Bhageerathi !

Jai Jai Gangae —— Hara Hara Gangae !

Utterkasi (U.P.)

10th Sept. 1969.   **Chinmaya**

"Tell, Never Teach, A Story"

A special and beautifully revealing article by Sree Swamiji himself for all Parents and Bala Vihar Sevaks/Sevikas.

Why Story-telling

Historically, never was there a time so badly cracked up. The maximum cleavage that we notice today is not in the political relationship between nations, nor in the social levels, nor in the economic opportunities, but it is certainly in the relationship in each home between the parents and their children. This is not only an ugliness in life, but it is a situation incomprehensibly tragic. The parents just breed, and they think that all their duties toward the growing generation are over if they feed and fatten them, clothe and groom them, and help them with education and to specialize.

Children at home are not pet animals which need only food and shelter. Why? Even sensitive animals, like dogs and cats, horses and elephants, demand some petting and its consequent emotional contentment to thrive, grow healthy and intelligent. How much more then, the most sensitive animal in the universe, Man, must need some personal attention, especially in his infancy. All delinquents are, without exception, created by negligent parents. In a moral government it would not be — I am sure — unjust if we were to punish the parents of delinquent children and send the children to remand homes and moral rehabilitation centres.

To plaster up these cracks, and to throw bridges across the widening gulf of differences between parents and their children, the elders must change their attitude towards their offspring.

The parents must spend each day at least half an hour with their children, reading aloud to them. It is for this purpose that we have the stories of PANCHATANTRA, and the endless volumes of PURANIC-STORIES. If the father himself were to fold up his newspaper, or return home a little earlier from his club, and, in a cheerful attitude of friendly CAMARADERIE, were to spend at least a few minutes with his children, we do not realize how immensely that would help them to rediscover their self-confidence and how much they will gain in their sense of security at home.

So long as they are infants, no doubt, they get almost a surfeit of attention from their parents. But as they grow up, how often we hear, "you are not a baby any longer, run out to play," or "don't hang on to my sari", or "what have children to do here; get out and play", or "don't spoil my pants".

These are innocent words, true, but how many of us realise that these thoughtless commands can murder the sensitive core of the growing children. The young need companionship; they demand attention, care, and love. Generally, the grown-ups are too busy or too much preoccupied. Through these unintentional, unmeant words, we perpetrate the greatest cruelties upon our children. We twist and bend and crumble their personality by these acts, and distort for ever all their relationships, even with their own parents, in the days to come.

The Art

Story-telling is an art that should be cultivated by all conscientious parents; it is an unavoidable must, and in fact, a girl who does not know how to tell stories, does not really deserve to be a complete mother. In fact, it should become one of the qualifications for taking up the true marital responsibilities.

Mastery of effective story-telling is certainly an art that can be cultivated by careful practice and attentive self-application. There is a treasure of joy for the story-teller, and a heritage of Good that the innocent, tiny listeners can gain from the story that is well-told to them.

Its Benefits

By spending half an hour each day with the children, reading out to them something interesting, their vocabulary improves, and they learn to talk in coherent and meaningful sentences––no more any baby-talk will issue forth from them. Also, this practice teaches them the art of listening, which will stand them in good stead when they grow up, not only in their early education, but also in their later life in the outer world of strife and strain.

Even when a parent has the occasion to tell stories, often the children may not sit quietly to listen to them. There is a reason for it. Ordinarily, the fathers and mothers do not know how to tell a story nor to attract and enchant the tiny tots with it. There are certain rules we must scrupulously follow in order to make a striking effect on the children with our stories.

(1)   First of all select carefully the BEST stories. Any story will not do; children must be exposed to the right type of stories which have a clear significance to THEM, and which must ring true and interesting to the CHILDREN'S MIND. The stories of PURANAS, carefully selected, and, if necessary, even retold in the BALA VIHAR-STYLE, can be unfailing and very effective.

(2)   While telling the story, let the narration build up the story slowly but very steadily. The story-teller should not run away from the story, and even if one does so, one must dutifully come back straight to the story from the pertinent and cheerful digression. The explanatory side-lights must vividly throw a more brilliant beam upon the main theme—the central story.

(3)   Often the elders are self-conscious that they are talking to the tiny tots, so they often repeat what has been already fully described. Children are sensitive to elders' condescensions and quickly feel a hurt vanity. Unconsciously, they "close up", and thereafter, the story runs on, but the child is left totally unaffected by the theme or its details.

Avoid the Pitfalls

Equally to be avoided at all costs are some other pitfalls, commonly encountered by story-tellers. The entire effect of a well-chosen and beautiful story can be totally destroyed by some of the unwitting mishandling of this tender art. That is why we find very often that when our neighbour tells our children the same story which we had ourselves told them many times, they sit up, thrilled anew, their faces shining with a fresh surprise and joy !

(1)   Children, in their innocent years, do not expect nor do they look forward to unnecessarily long descriptions, or any winding streams of wordy narrations. They need but some varied details, carefully given and painted with the barest minimum strokes, to bring out the full picture from their imaginative mind. They are, by their very nature, fancifully creative and our words should only stimulate—not clog—their minds with information, data and details.

An exhaustive treatment becomes too heavy and serious stuff for the children, especially for the junior tots in our BALA VIHARS. Even the seniors should not be gorged with over-detailed, unending descriptions and crazy and deliberately drawn out narrations. Let us be simple and straight and let us use an humble, plain but able vocabulary. All stories too rich with a wealth of detail do not run smoothly nor can their main theme easily flow. Children can be readily held in attention only by the mesmeric enchantment of the rhythm in the movements of the theme of the story.

(2)   While etching the movements of the story on the wonder-mind of the innocent children, be careful of the words employed and their possible suggestions in the minds of the children. Totally avoid situations describing indiscipline, vandalism, cruelty, disobedience, unheroic escapism, etc., in the heroes of the stories. In fact, quickly glide over these even if they be in the villain; let not the negative values even unintentionally take root in the children's hearts.

(3)   Please don't employ science in the stories. No doubt, children must be introduced to the mysteries of the Universe and the glories of science. But let not the story be loaded with these. While listening to the story a child is in a different mood, as children alone can be. They are thrilled by their love for the fantasia. Their imagination lights up. Their wide-eyed joys are a-kindled. Their divine enchantment of pleasure during the story-listening-hour is too sacred to be molested by roughly marshalled facts and data, crude details, and cute laws of nature. Children are, at such moments, in the very lap of nature gliding on incredible patterns surging in their own hearts— winged angels of the GODDESS OF KNOWLEDGE. Let them remain in their native glory; let us not shock them in the hope that they may become scientists or artists or politicians of this muddy world.

(4)   Similarly, let us not try to analyse the characters, or rationalise the situations. True, these are days of psychological analysis, and scientific enquiries every where, and I have often listened to good-intentioned parents spreading thickly such exhaustive treatment of stories, and we can watch how the children's faces instinctively become cloudy as their enthusiasm dies away.

Let the children do the character reading for themselves! — they demand no rationale for the story and its incidents. Take them on the wings of the story into their own ecstatic realm of innocent dreams and imaginary world of quaint, exaggerated and heroic men of noble actions. To little ones it does not matter whether the hero is Shree Rama in the jungle, Sree Krishna on the Jamuna banks, a wolf in the woods, or a frog in its hole near a wayside pond !!

(5)   Lastly, never preach through the stories. "DON'T PREACH, BUT PORTRAY," is the tested, golden rule. FULLY narrate. CLEARLY describe. VIVIDLY portray. ELOQUENTLY tell. But never, never should we, in our over-anxiety, try to PREACH a moral. Just in passing we may mention the moral value, but then pass on quickly; please don't tarry over it. The very story in the growing child will, by itself, instil the great truths and higher values of life as time passes on. We should never exploit story-telling for preaching.

Selection of Stories

(1)   The main considerations in selecting the right type of stories are the audience, the occasion, and the purport.

(a)   The audience may be boys or girls. Perhaps they are the junior children, or the senior group, or a mixed group. THE STORY MUST BE SO SELECTED AS TO HOLD THE ATTENTION AND SUSTAINED ENTHUSIASM OF ALL THE TINY LISTENERS IN FRONT OF YOU AT ANY GIVEN TIME.

(b)   Also, the story must be appropriate to the occasion; a birthday party, a picnic, a journey, a marriage celebration, or a religious festival, or our regular BALA VIHAR meetings, or a combined meeting of the children and their parents. The same story may not suit all occasions.

(c)   Lastly, the selection of the story must depend upon the purport in the mind of the story-teller; to correct the children or to generate heroism; to inspire confidence, or to evoke generosity, or it may be to bring out the spirit of forgiveness in the heart of the listeners.

It may be just to soothe a child to rest and sleep, or to console him at his loss, or to encourage him to make a large-hearted sacrifice. The aim to be achieved should determine the choice of the story.

(2) Apart from these considerations the story selected must be subtly placed in a suitable atmosphere. In summer, let your story bring in rains; on rainy days, let the sun lash out; and in winter, let the cloudless sky, bright with the rising sun, and the dancing spring, touching magic on the tress, bring warmth and fragrance into the nostrils of the listening tots. The innocent children will bask in the unconscious enchantment of the atmosphere of a rightly chosen story.

(3) Children have boundless energy, and to keep physically quiet for even a short interval, is to them unnatural, insufferable. And yet, I have kept them with me for hours, quieter than sometimes the elders. The secret is to give the anxious listeners plenty of action in the story.

Let them dream of impossible distances, endless exertions, noble actions, heroic deeds, courageous undertakings, while listening to the stories. These mental activities painted for them through the gushing noisy flood of actions in the story, will make them quiet physically, as they are following mentally the hero of the action-packed story. The story-teller should, by his vivid words, clearly communicate the heaving scenes of panting actions to the enchanted bosom of the attentive child.

(4) Keep moving. Never lag. Don't pause. Don't jay-walk through story, hesitatingly building it up as it is being told. The story must in a steady trot, move—move towards a definite conclusion—galloping constantly up to the crisis and down into the valley of denouement. Again with a fresh hope, let the story pick up energy and courage to 'get up' and fight the problems, and thus let it move on and on, to the refreshing end of success and joy, rewarding the good, and ultimately punishing the evil.

Let there be no blocks enroute. And don't leave the child in doubt at the end. The story must conclude on a positive note of reward at the end of all the trials in life. The stories of DHRUVA, of PRAHLADA, or even SREE RAMA, are typical examples of such perfect narrations, which through sustained actions, dash forward, in graceful strides, to the optimistic and sunny summit of a definite conclusion: always ending in rich reward for the Good.

Fundamentals of Story-telling

(1) It is true, as parents, we are not born story-tellers; a very blessed few of us alone have the faculty naturally with us. But no loving adult should find it impossible to develop this art; actually every one of us has this faculty dormant in us. Only each of us would need different amounts of practice to bring this story-telling faculty into full bloom. Take it seriously; and practice it diligently. No one can fail in this.

(2) Having selected the appropriate story, tell it to yourself many times. Each time you tell the story, be yourself among the children, and listen! Identify mentally with the children, and hear your own narration, as they would hear it. You will instinctively correct your vocabulary, style, arrangement of details, and the tone of delivery. All these are important.

The best time to repeat the stories to yourself is at night when you are in bed, with the lights off. In that darkened room, let the BALA VIHAR children crowd around you, up to the ceiling; their eager faces lit up; with joyous expectations. Now you tell the story. Let a few loving and affectionate antennae from your heart try to contact and receive the reactions playing in the children's bosom. You will discover how easily you would polish and effectively re-arrange the narration, which is certain to suit the children's heart.

(3) It is also important that the story-teller should not be an inert radio set blistering the ears of his listeners with the monotonous recitation of the story. Let the story be rendered "living" and vivid by

appropriate gestures; remember, and this is very important, there should not be a single, unnecessary gesture. Purposeless gestures will distract the attention of the children—they will shift their attention from the flow of the story to the mad rhythm of the wild gestures.

(4) Know the story well. It is a psychological tragedy for the child to hear a part of a story and then to live in wonder and confusion, because the story-teller forgot the rest of the story. The poor child is awakened to recognise a situation and a personality in the story; to leave the child there as a neglected orphan, is to bring a mental problem to the carefree child to solve for himself, in his endless imaginations. This is criminal, crude, cruel, to say the least.

(5) You, as the story-teller, must feel the story. Unless you are yourself in it, as its very flesh and blood, the story will be a dead, decayed, dried up skeleton — horrible, dreadful, offensive. Give it life; enliven it by your sincerity and enthusiasm, your cheer and pleasure in narrating it to the children. These are contagious emotions. Children will get them from you, and thereafter, you will find you are drawing from them these very same feelings, in a larger measure.

(6) Be natural, and don't pose. Renounce all the artificial dignity and vanity of being an adult. Be yourself a child. Identify with them totally; think as they would: feel as they alone can. Be innocent and carefree as they always are. They, very instinctively, will come to recognise the child in you. The walls that separate the adult from the child, crumble down, and an ecstatic harmony is established. This adjustment between you and your listeners is an unavoidable prerequisite in all successful story-telling.

(7) Also be graphic. YOU don't tell the story; let your WORDS give it birth. Your words should paint for them the scenes, the situations, the feelings, and the personae. Make them all fabulously colourful, vivid and breathing with exciting life and the joy of living.

This doesn't mean that you must give elaborate description of nature, or exhaustive analysis of characters while telling the story. In fact, these you should never employ; a single flower will become a garden to the child; a few trees will make a forest for him; a bird, on the branch of the mango-tree is springtime for the child listening to the story. Just a hint —all the rest, the child, in his love of the fantastic, with his imagination and stored up pictures of his past experiences, will create for himself.

(8) Lastly, I have watched many of our Group-Sevaks telling the right kind of story, with the right words, gestures, graphically enough, and with full feeling. Yet, the children do not "take". Why? There is a sane reason. When each eager face turns up to you, with his heart geared to listen to the story, he expects you, not only to tell the story, but to tell the story to HIM. Each child wants the story to be told to HIM PERSONALLY. If the story-teller looks only into the faces of those who are sitting in the front row, or nearest to her, then the others who are behind feel neglected. This feeling is very poignant in them. They are behind only because there was no space for every child to be in the front row. Therefore, during the narrations, shift your eyes, and look at every row; smile with your eyes at every child; let him feel that he alone is the ONE to whom the story is being told.

If a sincere and loving BALA VIHAR SEVIKA were to note carefully these ideas, and practise diligently, she can grow in her sacred faculty of story-telling.

TELL, NEVER TEACH, A STORY. Children learn more BY A STORY, well told, than what we teach them THROUGH A STORY.

And, in fact, who is there who wouldn't tell a story? Only all can't tell them effectively without training. With a little practice, why shouldn't you be one of the best story-tellers in the Chinmaya Mission?

"We, the elders — parents and teachers, elder brothers and sisters — have the responsibility to provide for our children this much of education that they may come out into the fields of life wfth full confidence in themselves and a right knowledge of the world and the life therein. If one does not know the rules of the game and what is expected of himself, he cannot be truly a player in that given game, nor can he be expected to play in team spirit. When such an individual does not know what are the rules of life, and what exactly is the game of striving in this world, he must necessarily be a nuisance, and we should not expect him either to play the game of national endeavour or to contribute to the team spirit for the world unity.. . . .

Sree Swamiji

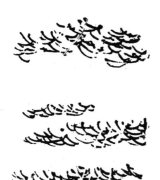
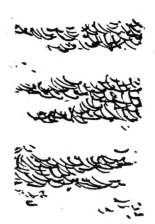

Prayer

उद्धव-

नमोऽस्तु ते महायोगिन् प्रपन्नमनुशाधिमाम् ।
यथा त्वच्चरणांभोजे रति:स्यादनपायिनी ॥

स्क. 11 अ. 29 श्लो. 40

Oh ! Maha Yogin !
Protect me, who am
surrendered to Thee.
May I be blessed
that my ecstacy at
Thy-Feet be
ever with me.

प्रह्लाद-

नह्यच्युतं प्रीणयतो बह्वायासोऽसुरात्मजा: ।
आत्मत्वात्सर्वभूतानां सिद्धत्वादिह सर्वत: ॥

स्क. 7 अ. 6 श्लो. 19

Dear Children of Asuras !
To please Achyuta
is the easiest work;
for, He is the Self
in the heart
of all Creatures,
and He is
ever-present, everywhere.

HARI OM

PART I

Parikshit Meets Kali

The Pandavas ruled in Hastinapura for a long time. They ruled under the king-ship of Yudhishtira and under the protection of Sri Krishna. But when the Lord left the earth altogether, they became despondent and retired to the Himalayas to lead lives of austerity and penance.

Parikshit, the grandson of the Pandava prince Arjuna, was placed on the throne of Hastinapura. He was a wise and noble ruler, and worked hard for the welfare of his people.

One day, he was strolling on the banks of the river Saraswati when he saw a strange sight. A lowly man, dressed in royal clothes, was kicking and torturing a white bull. A cow was standing close by and shedding tears. The bull had lost three of its legs, and the wicked man was about to cut off its fourth leg too.

Parikshit was very angry when he saw this. He turned to the man and said, "How dare you ill-treat these poor innocent creatures? Do you not know that I am King of this land, and that I can punish you even with death?" Then he turned to the trembling and shivering bull and cow and spoke to them very kindly and soothing them, enquired how the bull had lost its three legs.

The bull bowed its head before the king and said, "O King. You wonder who has caused my suffering. The answer to this even I do not know. Some say that beings in their ignorance cause their own happiness or sorrow. Others say it is due to their past *Karmas*. I do not know which is true".

Parikshit was surprised to hear the bull speak. He thought deeply. The realisation came to him that the bull was none other than *Dharma* or virtue; the cow was Mother Earth and the wicked man was *Kali* – the spirit of the *Kali Yuga*: the Iron Age of our times.

Parikshit then said to the bull, "You are indeed (the personification of) *Dharma*. Your four legs are Purity, Austerity, Charity and Truthfulness. Of these you have lost three legs, namely Purity, Austerity and Charity. You are now standing on Truthfulness alone, and this too, *Kali* was about to crush".

Saying this, Parikshit turned to *Kali* with his sword drawn and was about to cut off his head, when *Kali* fell at his feet and begged to be heard. Now a king cannot kill any creature which asks for his protection. So Parikshit had to listen to him. Then

स तु ब्रह्मऋषेरंसे गतासुमुरगं रुषा ।
. . . . निधाय पुरमागमत् ॥   (स्क. 1 अ. 18 श्लो. 30)

The King in anger put a dead serpent on the neck of the Brahma-Rishi and went away to his city.

Parikshit and Samika

Kali said, "I am to be the ruler of the next age (*Kali Yuga*) which will be full of cruelty and falsehood. Such is the will of the Lord. So please spare my life".

Parikshit was touched by *Kali's* humility and said, "Go. I grant you your life, but let me not see you anywhere while I am ruling the kingdom". *Kali* pleaded and said, "But I must live somewhere. Give me *some* place to live in". So Parikshit allowed him to live in all houses for gambling and drinking, places where there is cruelty to women and animals and centres where gold is acquired and hoarded. To these he added the fields of falsehood, pride, jealousy, enmity and lust, where *Kali* flourished and prospered.

Now that we know the places where this wicked *Kali* resides, we must try to avoid them, and, like King Parikshit, we must try and restore to the poor bull, its three lost legs – Purity, Austerity and Charity.

KING PARIKSHIT IS CURSED

One day, King Parikshit had gone hunting, deep into the jungle, all by himself. The hunt grew exciting, and he lost all sense of time. He had now come to a thick, dark part of the jungle. After some time he felt hungry and thirsty. He wandered about in search of water. This search took him deeper and deeper into the forest. One can imagine, therefore, his relief and happiness when he suddenly came across the hermitage of a well-known sage called Samika.

Parikshit looked all around him but could see no one. Then, in one part of the ashrama, he saw the sage sitting in Samadhi. His eyes were closed, his body was erect, he was not conscious of the world outside. In fact he was in deep meditation. But Parikshit did not realize this. He went up to him and asked for a drink of water. But the sage did not reply. How could he, when he was so deeply absorbed in meditation? And yet, Parikshit asked him a second time for water. Samika, however, sat motionless and erect, completely unaware of the thirsty king.

Now Parikshit thought to himself, "This fellow is only pretending. How can he not hear my request for water? Let me see how great his concentration is." So he picked up a dead snake from nearby and placed it around the Rishi's neck. This was not at all a nice thing to do. Yet Samika remained perfectly calm and fully concentrated in his meditation.

A few yards away from the hermitage was a small stream. Here the sage's son, a young boy called Sringi, had gone to fetch water. As he was returning, he saw what had happened at the ashrama. He was very angry and hurt at the insult to his holy father. The boy himself had much spiritual power. As Parikshit was about to leave, Sringi sipped off a little water from his palm*, and in a thundering voice called out,

---

* *Achamana* – This is symbolical. Water stands for all names and forms. Without water nothing will have a shape and therefore, name. These names and forms always disturb our minds.

"Sipping a little water" – (*Achamana*) thus represents "consuming all mental disturbances". – With a fully concentrated mind, the boy wished the cruel death of the king who had insulted his father.

"Obeying my command, on the seventh day from today, a powerful serpent, called Takshaka, will bite to death this proud Kshatriya who has insulted my holy father." And he wept bitterly at the insult to his father.

So when Samika came back to consciousness, he found his son lamenting loudly. He asked him what had happened. Sringi told him what King Parikshit had done and the curse he (Sringi) had pronounced upon him. When he heard the story, Samika scolded him and said, "Son, you should not have been so harsh. Kings are different from us. They carry the entire burden of the country on their shoulders. It is difficult to find a king as good as Parikshit. Besides, he had come to us only for rest and refreshment. He meant no harm. One wrong cannot be set right by another. O Lord, pray forgive my foolish son. Everything is now in Your hands."

Never once did the noble sage even think of the way Parikshit had insulted him! His heart was so full of divine love. In Parikshit he saw only the good, kind and just king, and not the man who had shown disrespect to a great Rishi. Such then are the noble, large-hearted sages of our land!

PARIKSHIT MEETS SUKA

When King Parikshit went back to his palace, he felt sorry for his bad behaviour towards the Saint. He sat and thought over his action. He remembered the divine glow on the sage's face, and again he was sorrowful. He welcomed the curse of Sringi, for he thought, "Ah ! This is a just punishment for my sins. I had become very attached to my kingdom and my people. Now that I know that my end is near, I can spend my last days hearing the stories of the Lord and in meditating upon His divine glories."

Then he called to him his son Janamejaya, and handed over his kingdom to him, and went to live on the banks of the sacred river Ganga, and decided to meet his death peacefully, with his mind fixed on the Lord.

Here, on the Ganges banks, Parikshit was visited by a number of holy sages and Rishis. Among them were Vyasa, Vasishta, Agastya, Angiras, Maitreya, and many others. Parikshit showed them due respect and asked for their blessings. As they were all engaged in conversation upon the Lord's glories, the revered young sage Suka came. He, the son of Vyasa, was only sixteen years old. He wore no clothes and his face glowed, his eyes shone; for although he was very young, he had infinite knowledge and wisdom and an unceasing devotion for the Lord.

All the assembled sages stood up to receive Suka, for he was held in great esteem by them. Parikshit touched his feet in deep respect and stood before him with folded hands. He felt extremely happy that he had the blessings of all these sages in his last days. To Sukadeva he said, "O great master, I do not deserve the honour you have shown me by coming here. Please teach me the way of obtaining freedom from this chain of birth and death. Tell me what a man who is about to meet his death should do. Teach me, O holy one."

Suka smiled at him and advised him on how to meditate. Then he proceeded to tell him the story of the Lord's divine play in the universe.

Let us imagine this beautiful scene. The Ganges is flowing by, calm and serene. A slight breeze stirs the leaves of the trees. On the holy banks a noble and virtuous king has spread the *kusa* grass and is seated upon it. All around him are the greatest Rishis of the land. They are listening to the beautiful story of the Lord as the divine Sukadeva relates it in his deep, melodious voice. Even the birds and animals of the forest have gathered around to listen. Let us also listen to this story and learn to make our hearts pure enough to receive its message.

VARAHA AVATARA

Brahma is the Creator of the entire Universe. He created the first man and woman. The man was called Swayambhuva Manu and the woman was called Satarupa. He commanded Manu and Satarupa to go forth and multiply. Manu bowed his head before his father and said, "O father, I shall indeed obey your command and beget children. But tell me where am I to keep them? The *Bhu* (earth) lies buried deep in the oceans of *Pralaya*. Only you can bring it above the waters. Therefore, father, help me."

Brahma sat and thought about what was to be done. When he was thus brooding, a Boar no bigger than the size of the thumb suddenly sprang out of his right nostril. Immediately it started growing till it had acquired a huge and gigantic form. The Boar roared out aloud. The dwellers of the heavens worshipped Him in awe. For they knew Him to be the incarnation of Sri Narayana Who had assumed this form for the good of the world.

The Boar then dived deep down into the oceans. He has, as you know, a very good sense of smell. Using it down below in the waters, he was able to smell out where *Bhu* was. As he was lifting it up, he was attacked by the vicious daitya king, Hiranyaksha. The Boar was earaged at this. He pierced and clawed and tore open the daitya king. Then he brought earth above the surface of the water, delicately balanced on his powerful tusks. The devas who were watching this, burst forth into hymns and songs in praise of Sri Narayana.

KASYAPA

Let us now see who this Hiranyaksha was.

It was *sandhya** time. The Rishi Kasyapa was just finishing his worship by pouring the last oblation into the secrificial fire. Slowly, the sun grew a fierce red and prepared to bed down for the night. The Rishi sat down to meditate on the one Lord, the Supreme Brahman.

Just then his wife, Diti, the daughter of Daksha, approached him and said, "Lord I am tormented by my hunger for your love. Please therefore, come and satisfy my desire.'

---

* Sun-set

.... युवां वासं न चार्हथः

रजस्तमोभ्यां रहिते पादमूले मधुद्विषः

पापिष्ठामासुरीं योनि बालिशौ यातमाश्वतः ॥   (स्क. 7 अ. 1 श्लो 37, 38)

"You both (Jaya and Vijaya) do not deserve to remain at the divine feet of Lord Vishnu. Oh ignorant ones! Both of you shall take birth in an asuric womb in the world."

Expulsion of Jaya and Vijaya from Vaikuntha

Kasyapa looked up from his seat of meditation and saw the look of lust in his wife's eyes. But he said to her kindly, "Wait for another hour, Diti. This is the time when Rudra, the terrible, roams about with his retinue of *pisacas**. "He himself takes the form of a *pisaca* and covers his body with ashes, to teach people indifference to their worthless bodies, which they decorate with fine silks, flower garlands and cosmetics. The body is verily the food for dogs. Rudra spurns wealth. *Maya* is his slave. He is the all-powerful Supreme Being. Let us now keep our minds pure and show him due respect by meditating upon the Lord".

But Diti would not listen to him. So Kasyapa obliged her. He then went and bathed in cool, purifying waters and, once more, sat down to meditate.

By now Diti was ashamed of herself. Trembling, she went and prostrated before her husband. With tears in her eyes, she said, "Holy sage! I have been in the wrong. But please do not let Rudra destroy the seed you have placed in my womb. May Shiva the Almighty Lord of the universe heed my prayer and grant His protection."

Kasyapa then said to her, "Diti, your wrong has been two-fold — you have been the victim of your own desire and you have disobeyed me. Two sons will be born to you. They will both be extremely wicked. They will murder the innocent, violate chastity of women, and insult great Rishis. When the three worlds can no longer bear their deeds of rape and violence, the Lord Himself will incarnate to kill them."

Diti was struck with remorse. She kept her twin sons in her womb for a hundred years, knowing that they would be a trouble to the devas and the Rishis. Kasyapa's seeds, however, were very powerful on account of the following incident which had taken place in Vaikuntha.

JAYA AND VIJAYA

Vaikuntha is Sri Vishnu's abode. Sri Vishnu and His attendants live there in an atmosphere of pure *sattwa*. They see the same oneness everywhere and observe no distinctions whatsoever.

One day, Brahma's mind-born sons, the four Sanatkumaras, decided to visit Lord Vishnu in Vaikuntha. They looked like small five-year old boys, even though they were the oldest living beings. This was on account of their great *tapas*. The sages passed through the first six gates of Vaikuntha unchallenged. At the seventh gate they were stopped by two gate-keepers of equal age and shining form, adorned with golden crowns and other sparkling ornaments. These two gate-keepers called Jaya and Vijaya, stopped the Sanatkumaras with their clubs, thinking them to be small children. The Rishis were greatly pained at this and said, "How can you make distinctions in Vaikuntha where a uniform oneness prevails? How can you suspect danger to the Lord in Whom the entire universe rests? Indeed you are not fit to live in this *sattwic* sphere. We shall not be too harsh on you because you are His servants. You shall descend to earth into the world of lust, anger, and greed from which spring all diversity."

---
* spirits

Jaya and Vijaya realised their mistake. Immediately they prostrated before the Sanatkumaras and begged to be forgiven. "Be it as you have said," they said. "Grant that we descend at the earliest and that even during our stay on earth we shall ever remember the Lord."

Now Sri Vishnu, because He knows everything, knew what had happened outside. With Lakshmi by His side, He hurried out to the gate. In wonder, the Sanatkumaras saw Him on Whom they had always meditated in their hearts. They prostrated before Him and gazed upon His resplendent shining form and could not take their eyes away from Him. Again they prostrated before Him and said, "Forgive us, Bhagavan, for having cursed Your servants. May our curse not have any effect."

Bhagavan answered, "It is I who should ask your forgiveness. For I am indirectly responsible for my servants' actions. Your curse shall have effect indeed, for it was not you who spoke, but I Who spoke through you. Jaya and Vijaya will be born as asuras on earth but their minds, intensified with anger and hatred, will be constantly united with Me.".

To the door-keepers He said, "Go forth and be not afraid. All will be well with you. Soon, when the time comes, I will Myself come to redeem you. Then with your minds purified, you will return to Vaikuntha in My service."

Jaya and Vijaya lost the glow on their faces and became dull and dark. They descended on to the earth and entered Kasyapa's seeds in Diti's womb.

HIRANYAKSHA

After remaining in their mother's womb for a hundred years, the two asuras were born in Kasyapa's ashrama. Signs boding ill and bad omens appeared everywhere. The mountains trembled. Storms uprooted trees and wrecked houses. The skies caught fire. Meteors fell upon the earth and caused great damage everywhere. Animals ran hither and thither in great fear, human beings quailed and trembled. Cows yielded blood instead of milk."

Kasyapa named the two asuras as Hiranyaksha and Hiranyakasipu. They grew not only in size and strength, but also in pride and vanity. They were a terror wherever they went. They murdered people, slaughtered animals, troubled virtuous women, disturbed the sacrifices of the Rishis and abused them. Everyone trembled at the very mention of their names.

One day Hiranyaksha, tall as a mountain, his hair long and matted, his teeth dripping blood, brandishing his club over his head, entered Indraloka and roared out a challenge. But he found no one there. Everyone, including Indra was in hiding. So he went into the ocean and challenged its ruler, Varuna. Varuna was old, wise and shrewd. He said to Hiranyaksha, "I am now old. I have given up fighting. My mind is fixed upon Sri Vishnu, the Lord of the Universe. Why don't you challenge Him? He is sure to kill your pride and reduce you to nothing."

Hiranyaksha, thirsting for a good fight, went in search of Sri Vishnu and was told that He was now incarnated as a Boar, and was lifting the earth from the oceanic waters. So he dived down and perceiving the Divine Boar lifting the earth on its tusks, laughed out aloud and sneered, "Aha! Now I have you at last. Till now you have been defeating the asuras by remaining invisible. Now that you are visible, I shall fight and kill you and avenge all the asuras you have killed."

Lord Vishnu (the Boar), ignored him and continued lifting the earth up. Hiranyaksha followed Him, all the while jeering that He was a coward, fleeing from a worthy challenge. After coming to the surface, Sri Vishnu firmly placed the earth and gave it some of His own strength so that it may continue functioning on its own.

Then a fierce struggle started between the two. It was a long and serious fight. Hiranyaksha was aided by all the asuras. They all resorted to magical tricks and foul play. The Lord defeated them at every turn, till at last, with one final blow, the daitya was killed. His eyes popped out, blood spurted forth from his huge body, he spun round and round and finally fell with a mighty thud that set the earth shaking.

The beings of the three worlds wept in joyous relief, and rejoicingly burst into praise of Mahavishnu.

Swayambhuva Manu and Satarupa were the first man and woman, remember? They had two sons and three daughters. The sons' names were Uttanapada and Priyavrata, and the daughters' names were Akuti, Devahuti and Prasuti. Now let us read the stories of some of these children of Manu.

KARDAMA AND DEVAHUTI

Kardama was a great sage who did penance on the banks of the river Saraswati for many years. He prayed to the Lord to bless him with a good and beautiful wife. After many scores of years Lord Vishnu appeared to him and said, "I am pleased with your worship and penance. On the third day from today, Manu will come and give you his beautiful daughter in marriage. You shall give her nine daughters who will be the mothers of great Rishis, and a son who will be none other than Me. Then you will spend the rest of your days in meditation till finally you see Me alone in the entire universe, and the entire universe in Me."

Now Devahuti had grown to be a very beautiful and charming girl. Her parents became anxious to find her a suitable husband. So one day Manu mounted his golden chariot, took his wife and daughter along, and travelled through various lands and places looking for a good match for Devahuti.

As they were travelling, they came to the banks of the river Saraswati. They saw here a beautiful ashrama. Creepers climbed the trunks of trees. Flowers were pretty, delicate and fragrant. Animals roamed freely and birds chirruped joyously. To one side was a cool plantain grove.

In this hermitage, they saw a young man whose face glowed with the glory of his *tapas*, pouring oblations into the sacred fire. Manu alighted from his chariot and going up to the young man said "O holy sage! As directed by the sage Narada, I have come to you to offer you my daughter in marriage. So far, only in your learning, wisdom and youth have we found a match for her beauty, virtues and character. Pray accept her as your wife and help-mate."

Kardama looked at Devahuti. He was charmed by her youth and fresh beauty. Devahuti too, liked the sage at the very first sight. So Kardama said, "I am indeed honoured by your offer. Your daughter is, indeed, all that you say and even more. Even her shining ornaments look pale in comparison to her own matchless radiance. Yet I will accept her only on one condition. The moment a son is born to us, who will be a ray of Lord Vishnu, I will go away, and, undisturbed, I will perform penance for Self-realization."

Manu and Satarupa were delighted and soon, Devahuti was given in marriage to Kardama.

For a number of years they lived a hard life of penance and sacrifice. Kardama would be engaged in performing *tapas* and Devahuti would faithfully serve him as a dutiful wife. Kardama taught her how to meditate. She was happy to serve her husband, but nevertheless she desired to have children.

So after many, many long years of penance, to Kardama and Devahuti were born nine girls. They were all virtuous and beautiful maidens. Yet, Devahuti's heart longed for a son. This longing of hers was soon fulfilled. The Lord entered her womb and was born in the world as Kapila. At the time of his birth, the devas and gandharvas* showered flowers from heaven. Narada, Brahma, the four Sanatkumaras and the nine Prajapatis, all come to visit Kardama and Devahuti. They congratulated them on the lotus-eyed, golden-haired beauty of their baby son.

Then amidst all the rejoicing, Kardama gave his nine daughters in marriage to the nine Prajapatis and they, after some time, went back to their own ashramas.

Kardama knew that now the time had come for him to go and do greater penance. He went round his son, the divine Lord, and prostrated before Him. Then he went away from the ashrama and became a monk.

KAPILA

Kapila soon became famous as a divine teacher and a sage of wonderful merit. He was the founder of the famous *Sankhya* philosophy. Naturally, Devahuti was proud of her learned son.

---

* celestial beings

One day she approached him and said, "Son, you are dearer to me than life itself. You have the knowledge of everything in this world. Will you not teach me how to gain freedom from birth and death? I learnt much from your father many years ago. Now I wish to learn from you."

Kapila looked affectionately at his mother and smiled. "Mother," he said, "I will gladly teach you what I know of gaining freedom from this cycle (of birth and death). Listen."

Then he told her that first and foremost one must have a pure heart and a loving devotion for God. He said, "Only they can claim eternal freedom, who love God as much as they love themselves, as tenderly as they love their own children, who trust Him as a beloved friend and revere Him as the supreme Guru, and above all who worship Him with unceasing devotion."

Kapila then told her about God's play in the universe as Purusha and Prakriti, about the three modes of the mind (*gunas*) and taught her the yoga of meditation.

Then, teaching her about divine love, he said, "Mother, those people who have hatred, anger and jealousy in their hearts worship God selfishly, as something apart from them. Such people have *tamasic* devotion.

"Those who pray to Him for material gains have a *rajasic* devotion for Him.

"But those who love Him for the sake of love, not because they want anything, theirs is the *sattwic*, the highest kind of devotion. In this kind of *bhakti*, the mind runs towards Bhagavan continuously, like the Ganga flowing into the sea.

"Mother, to purify the heart, one must obey the following rules of life.

"The duties of life must be performed by everybody. Work must be looked upon as worship. One must chant God's name more and more.

"One must see the blessed Lord in all creatures and be friendly to all, and kind to the poor and the helpless.

"One must be humble, devoted and self-controlled and must pass one's days in listening and chanting the Lord's glories."

Thus Kapila taught his mother many wonderful things about the Lord's divine nature and how one could reach Him. Devahuti followed her son's teachings faithfully and soon discovered the Lord of the Universe – Jagadeeswara – seated within her own heart.

Kapila left the ashrama soon after this and went high up into the Himalayas, where, they say, he still meditates and prays for the welfare of the world.

These teachings of Kapila made it possible for Devahuti to reach the state of sainthood. If we follow them sincerely, we too can become better and purer human beings.

SATI

Manu's third daughter, Prasuti, married Daksha, the Prajapati. She gave birth to sixteen daughters. They were all married to Lord Dharma except one of them whose name was Sati.

Sati was a great devotee of Lord Shiva. She worshipped him at all times with intense devotion. Ultimately, Shiva and Sati were married.

One day, Daksha decided to perform a huge sacrifice. All the gods, Rishis, sages, kings and celestials were invited to it. The day arrived. Everyone was seated in the hall which had been prepared for the sacrifice. The sacrificial trough had been dug. The materials for the sacrifice were kept ready in golden pots and platters. The Brahmin priests had all gathered. The *mantras* and incantations filled the air. At this moment the conches were sounded. Daksha entered the sacrificial hall. The entire assembly rose in respect. Daksha's head went up and his chest expanded in pride, as he saw the honour that all the gods and sages were showing him. And then his eye caught sight of two persons who had not stood up. They were Brahma, his father, and Shiva, his divine son-in-law. Daksha prostrated before Brahma and asked his blessings. He then looked at Shiva who continued to sit quietly. This Daksha could not bear.

He was terribly angry. He lost his temper and abused Shiva in front of all the guests. He said, "You are a shameless person! I know you are jealous of my wealth and position. I have never seen anyone more ungrateful than you. I have given you in marriage my gifted and accomplished daughter, and yet you have dared to show me disrespect."

To the devas he said, "Look at him. He knows no difference between purity and impurity, respect and disrespect. He roams around in the cremation grounds, his body covered with ashes. He should be called Ashiva, the inauspicious, and not Shiva, the auspicious." Then he poured a little water into his palm and sipped it up. The entire assembly looked shocked and horrified as he pronounced the curse, "Henceforth you will never get the share of any sacrifice. This should teach you a lesson."

All through this Shiva remained calm and composed, never uttering a single word in anger or protest. But one of his followers called Nandiswara, could not swallow this insult to his beloved Shiva. Quickly, he too sipped a little water and in turn cursed Daksha saying, "Shiva hates no one. It is Daksha who sees differences around him. He considers his body to be all in all. He will forever remain chained to the path of sacrifice and ritual. Being fond of the body, he will be extremely attached to women and he will soon acquire a face like that of a goat. The assembled Brahmins who support him will forever be caught up in the cycle of birth and death. They will crave wealth and worldly enjoyments. They will make a profession of their learning and *tapas*."

Bhringu, the leader of the Brahmins, uttered a counter curse on Nandi and the followers of Shiva. "They shall adorn their bodies with ashes and bones and with their hair loose, they shall frequent the cremation grounds. Those who forget that Narayana is at the root of all things in the world shall attain only the *tamasic* Shiva – the Lord of *bhutas* and *pisacas.*"

Now there was confusion all around. People had never heard such terrible curses before. Quietly, Shiva got up and left the hall. His followers too walked behind him. From that time onwards there was constant enmity between the followers of Shiva and those of Daksha.

Sometime later, Brahma made Daksha the head of the Prajapatis. Daksha's pride knew no bounds. He decided now to perform a yagna on a lavish scale. This was the Brihaspati yagna. To this sacrifice all the inhabitants of the three worlds were invited except Shiva and his divine consort, Sati.

Now when Sati heard of the elaborate preparations that were going on in her father's house, she also wanted to go and see it. Shiva pointed out to her that they had not been invited. She looked at him pleadingly and said, "Surely a daughter needs no invitation to visit her father's house. In the intense preparation of the yagna he must have forgotten to invite us. Besides, I so much want to see my mother and sisters again." So at last Shiva allowed her to go.

Dresssing herself up in her finest clothes, and accompanied by her own personal attendants, Sati set out for Daksha's house. It was a queer procession. Sati rode on Shiva's bull. Her maids went with her, singing, laughing, joking, their anklets making soft tinkling music. Shiva's attendants too, went along. They were the odd-looking *bhutas* and *pisacas*, their bodies covered with ashes and ornamented with skulls and bones. Thus this music-making, trumpet-blaring procession approached Daksha's palace. But no one came forward to receive Sati except her mother and sisters, who came out and embraced her. Her father even refused to look at her. Being afraid of Daksha, the other guests would not even talk to her. Sati felt uneasy at their strange behaviour. Then she looked around and saw that no yagna offering had been kept in the name of Shiva.

Her eyes sparkled and her lower lip trembled as she turned furiously on Daksha and said, "Shame on you! You have shown disrespect to Shiva in whose eyes all are equal. You have ignored Him on Whom all the yogis and devas meditate as the Supreme Brahman. I am indeed ashamed of this body which has come from you— you, who care not for the soul in your attachment for the body."

She then dressed herself up in yellow silk, made *achamana*,* and facing north, sat in a yogic posture. Then she closed her eyes, and concentrating the air and fire elements in her body, fixed her mind on the feet of Shiva. As the horrified guests looked on, her body suddenly caught fire and was soon reduced to ashes.

There was now a great furore and confusion in the hall of sacrifice. People ran here, there and everywhere. Even Daksha was sorry for what his stupidity had led to.

---

* Sipped water

ततः स्वभर्तुश्चरणांबुजासवं
जगद्गुरोश्चिन्तयती न चापरम् ।
ददर्श देहे हतकल्मषा सती
सद्यः प्रजज्वाल समधिनाग्निना ॥   (स्क. 4 अ. 4 श्लो. 27)

Uma then with a totally purified mind contemplated upon the sweet feet of her Lord, Parameshwara, and Sati saw nothing else in her body, and in the fire of Samadhi, her body burned up.

Sati, in a Yoga posture concentrates   air and fire elements in her body

Narada ran to tell Shiva what had happened. Shiva rose in a terrible fury and bit his lip in anger. He tore up a *jata** from his head and dashed it on the ground. From it sprang up the tall and terrible Virabhadra – reaching the heavens in height, dark as a thick black cloud, his three eyes flaming like the burning sun, his teeth terrible to look at, his hair as bright red as the glowing fire. He had a thousand hands, and in each hand he carried mighty weapons of destruction. Around his neck was a garland of human skulls. Standing there before Shiva, as if waiting to strike, he said, "What are your commands, O Lord?" Shiva said, "Go and lead my whole army. Put an end to Daksha and his sacrifice."

Like a dust-storm, Virabhadra and the warriors of Shiva descended upon the yagna. The priests and guests huddled together in fear – was it a hurricane? Or a band of robbers? What could be the cause of this approaching volume of dust? Before they could even think straight, the attendants of Shiva had started on their rounds of pollution and destruction. They broke the yagna implements and scattered them all over. They pulled down buildings, put out the sacrificial fires, ran after the Rishis and frightened the women. Those of Daksha's priests and supporters who tried to run away were stoned by the followers of Shiva. Some were tied down, some had their beards uprooted, some had their eyeballs pulled out and some had their teeth smashed in. Above all, using one of the implements of sacrifice Virabhadra cut off the head of Daksha. After thus completely destroying the place of the yagna, Virabhadra and Shiva's army returned to Mount Kailash.

The terrified devas now went to Brahma. Brahma and Vishnu who knew what was going to happen at Daksha's yagna had kept themselves away from it. Brahma scolded the devas for the way they had insulted Shiva. He said, "Did you not know that by a mere act of his will, Shiva can destroy the entire universe? The least you can do now is to go and beg for his forgiveness."

Then at the request of the devas, Brahma accompanied them to Mount Kailash. There, under a large *Vata*** tree, sat Lord Shiva, absorbed in *Yoga-samadhi*. His face glowed with the calmness and beauty of meditation. Brahma then requested Shiva to pardon Daksha and his followers, to return them back to life, and to allow them to complete the yagna. He said, "You are the Supreme Brahman. Let not your anger destroy these ignorant devas. They have learnt their lesson now. Henceforth all the remnants of the yagna offerings shall be yours. Accept them and let the sacrifice be completed."

Shiva stirred slightly and looked up with a smile. "I have nothing against Dakhsa. Why, he is as much an offender as an ignorant child is. But I have indeed taught a lesson to those who are led astray by *maya*. Let them know that I care not for sacrifices on the material level, that I attach no importance to the body whatsoever. The limbs of the devas shall be restored to them. Daksha's head was burnt up by the yagna implement. So let him have the head of a goat."

---

* matted lock of hair   ** Banyan

The davas were satisfied. They thanked Shiva and invited him to participate in the sacrifice. Brahma and Shiva went to the sacrifice together. Daksha, (who had regained life and now had a goat's head), welcomed Shiva with reverence. His mind was now wise and purified. The sacrifice was performed. Daksha sat in deep meditation, when, suddenly, on the wings of Garuda, Sri Vishnu appeared. Beautiful prayers of love and reverence burst forth from the lips of all. Lord Vishnu moved over to where Brahma and Shiva were standing. As they stood there, Brahma's face reflected the pride and happiness of paternal love, Vishnu shone with the very *sattwa* of his being, and Shiva glowed with the divine bliss of meditation.

Then Sri Vishnu spoke and said, "Only the ignorant see the difference between Shiva and Me. The wise know that Brahma, Shiva and I are one. The One assumes the three different aspects for the creation, preservation and destruction of the universe. He who worships even one, worships, in fact, all the three. Everything in the whole universe is nothing but the manifestation of this one great Truth. Nothing exists apart from It."

The devas and Rishis present were overwhelmed. They prostrated to the Triune and were blessed by the Lord's grace.

Such then is the story of Sati. She was born again as Parvati, the daughter of Himavan. After years of rigorous penance, she got married to Shiva.

DHRUVA

King Uttanapada was the first son of Manu. He had two wives, the elder Suniti and the younger Suruchi. Suniti had a son called Dhruva. Suruchi had a son called Uttama. Suruchi was very beautiful and so the king favoured her. But she had a terribly jealous and possessive nature. So much so, that she would not even let Uttanapada see Suniti or her son.

One day, Suruchi was sitting, laughing and chatting with the king and her son Uttama was playing on his lap. Just then Dhruva came into the room. He too, wanted to climb his father's knee and play with him. But the king, fearing the anger of Suruchi, paid no attention to him. Suruchi taunted the little boy and said, "I have no doubt that you are the king's eldest son. But to be in his favour is a different thing. For that you will have to take birth in my womb. Therefore, go and do penance, so that in your next life, you may be born as my son." Sadly, with tears in his eyes, Dhruva looked up at his father. But Uttanapada made no move to either embrace him or to hold him close, nay, not even to smile at him.

Now Dhruva, although only five years old, was of an extremely sensitive nature. He ran to his mother's apartments and clung to her legs, sobbing uncontrollably. The mother's heart in Suniti bled for him. She took him in her arms, smoothed back the locks of hair from his forehead, and kissed his tears away. She soothed him with soft, loving words and gentle whispers. When his lips had stopped quivering and he had become fairly calm, she said to him, "Do not grieve so, my son, at the words of your step-mother.

Remember, there is always justice in the eyes of God. Everyone must pay the price for his *karmas*, good or bad. You must feel sorrow for her rather than anger. Think of the one great truth she told you. Through penance, prayer and the grace of Narayana, everything is possible."

Dhruva, his eyes still bright with tears, looked up at his mother and said, "Who is this Narayana, mother? Where can I find Him?"

Suniti answered, "My son, He is called the Lotus-eyed One. He removes the miseries and fulfills the desires of those who renounce all and take refuge in Him. But He is not easily attainable. After years of strict austerity and penance, yogis have realized Him through intense devotion, seated deep within their own hearts."

Dhruva thought over his mother's words. That night, when everyone was fast asleep, he quietly stole out of the palace and made towards the deep, dark jungles. He walked thus for many days and nights without food, water or rest, crying out passionately, "Vaasudeva ! Narayana ! Where are You?" He asked the lions, tigers, bears and jackals of the forest if they had seen Narayana. They looked at him in amazement, shook their heads and walked away.

It is said in the *Shastras* that when one seeks the light to dispel the darkness in one's heart, the Lord sends to such a one a teacher who has Discovered his own inner Light.

Narada, the great sage, was once sitting, his mind blissfully dwelling upon the glories of God, when he heard the sincere cries of Dhruva for the vision of the Lord.

Narada, therefore, set out to meet the boy. He blessed him and tried to test his earnestness by saying, "My son. You are still too young to start off on your search for God. Go back to where you belong. People see God after many, many years, nay, many, many lives of striving. These are your days to enjoy. Go and lead a worthy life. Associate yourself with the good and the great. Be kind and generous to all. In your old-age, when your duties are over, you can meditate upon the Lord."

Dhruva folded his palms respectfully and said, "Revered sage! My burning desire is to realize God and to attain the highest goal in life. Pray show me the path."

Narada was now convinced that Dhruva was indeed a sincere seeker. He taught him Japa and showed him how a mind free from restlessness becomes available for meditation. He then taught him how to meditate and gave him the sacred *Dvadashakshara Mantra* – OM NAMO BHAGAVATE VASUDEVAYA – and asked him to meditate upon it constantly.

"Make your heart pure and free from all agitations," he said. "Feel His loving presence in your heart at all times. Meditate upon Him always. See Him only at all places, in all beings. Devote yourself entirely to his worship and even in this life you shall realize Him."

नारद –

जनन्याभिहितः पन्था स वै निश्रेयसस्य ते
भगवान् वासुदेवस्तं भज तत्प्रवणात्मना ॥   (स्क. 4 अ 8 श्लो 40)

Narada said: "The path of surrendering to Lord Vaasudeva, indicated by your mother is indeed the most effective . . . . . You seek Him alone with all your heart.

Narada and Dhruva

Narada then advised Dhruva to go to Madhuvanam on the sacred banks of the Yamuna, and there to practise meditation and to perform *tapas*. Dhruva prostrated before his teacher, and went to the seclusion of Madhuvanam to perform penance.

During the first few days his spirit was restless. But soon he found a boundless joy in meditation. He subjected himself to rigorous *tapas*. He undertook terrible fasts, eating only dried leaves and grass, sipping water once in nine days, and breathing only once in a while. He went into long spells of Samadhi. By the fifth month, he had lost all consciousness of the outer world and had entered deeper into meditation. He stopped all movements of his body and stood poised only on the big toe of one foot. The three worlds began to rock, so great was the force of his penance! The earth tilted at the point where his toe pressed the ground. When he stopped his breath in Samadhi, the breath of the three worlds also stopped, all but suffocating the living creatures.

The Lord, now thirsty for the darshan of His *bhakta*, mounted His Garuda and gracefully landed in front of him. Slowly, Dhruva opened his eyes. He was dazzled by the presence of the divine Lord. He prostrated "full length" but could not utter a single word, so struck was he by the resplendence of Sri Narayana!

The Lord, full of love and happiness, smiled, and in blessing touched Dhruva with His divine conch. Dhruva's heart was flooded with love and in supreme joy he sang the praises of the Lord – "Hail to You, Lord of the universe, Friend of the poor and the afflicted. Grant that I may ever revel in Your presence. Grant that my mind be ever engaged in contemplation of Your blissful feet. Grant me Thy own Eternal Being!"

भक्ति मुहुः प्रवहतां त्वयि मे प्रमङ्गो
भूयादनन्त महताममलाशयानाम् ।
येनाञ्जसोल्बणमुरुव्यसनम् भवाब्धि
नेष्ये भव गुण कथामृतपानमत्तः ॥

(May I enjoy the intimate fellowship, O Infinite Lord, of exalted souls, possessed of pure hearts and constantly devoted to You, so that I may easily cross the terrible ocean of this *samsar*, full of great perils; may I get drunk with the nectar of Your divine virtue and ennobling stories).

Narayana said, "My child. I know your heart. I grant you your boon. But now you will have to go back to your father and rule the kingdom till your allotted time upon the earth is over. Then you shall ascend to the celestial sphere where the devas, gandharvas and apsaras constantly chant My glories. Here you shall have a permanent unchanging place and shall be called the Dhruva Nakshatra. In later years, men will draw their guidance from you."

With this blessing the Lord disappeared.

Obeying His command, Dhruva set out on his journey. His father, mothers and brother, all came out in splendid chariots and carriages to welcome him. He prostrated before his father, bowed low before his mothers and embraced his brother. Suruchi begged

स वं धिया योगविपाकतीव्रया
हृत्पद्मकोशे स्फुरितं तडित्प्रभम् ।
तिरोहितं सहसेवोपलक्ष्य
बहिः स्थितं तदवस्थं ददर्श ॥

(स्क 4 अ 9 श्लो 2)

He in his heart, purified by his terrible Tapas, saw for a moment a brilliant flash of Light, which disappeared immediately. Therefore Dhruva opened his eyes and lo! saw Him standing in front in all glory.

Lord Vishnu and Dhruva

his forgivenness. Suniti embraced him with tears of joy in her eyes. There was great rejoicing throughout the country. Dhruva was led to the palace with great pomp and show.

Dhruva soon succeeded his father as the king. He ruled as a wise and noble ruler for many prosperous years. Towards the end, he left his home and palace, and retired to Badarika Ashrama in the Himalayas to regain the divine experience of his youth. He spent his days in daily prayers and meditations till finally he again lost his physical consciousness. When the time approached for him to give up his body, he saw a brilliant vision – a shining chariot and two of Lord Vishnu's attendants who conducted him to the celestial sphere of Vishnu-Loka to become the pole star. It has guided mankind in every age and to this day, the Hindus call it as the Dhruva Nakshatra.

KING PRITHU

Prithu was a descendant of Dhruva. He was not only a noble ruler but also a good man. When he was crowned as the king people spent many days in merry-making. One day while the festivities were still going on, news came to him that there was a terrible famine in his land. This famine was not only that of food and grains but also that of strength and beauty, art and music, love and goodness.

King Prithu was sad at the plight of his people and wondered why the earth had stopped her yields. At this time Mother Earth came up to him in the guise of a cow and said, "O noble king, I know what is the cause of your worry. I have all the seeds of the vegetables and herbs in my bosom. Had I brought them all out at one time there would have been nothing left for future yagnas. They are all now deep within me, rotting away. I cannot bring them up unless man makes the effort. If he is ready to exert himself I am ready to give him anything he desires."

Prithu and his subjects then levelled the land at the request of the earth and prepared it fully. Slowly, because of their sweat and toil, the vegetables and life-giving herbs started coming up. Mother Earth looked green and happy again. Man got his food and grains.

The Rishis got their food, the Vedas.

The devas got their *amrita* in a golden pot and also the energies of the body (*sarira*), mind (*mana*) and sense organs (*indriyas*).

The daityas got their wines and intoxicating drinks.

The gandharvas and apsaras received fragrance, beauty and sweetness in a lotus vessel.

The siddhas got yogic powers.

The vidyadharas got knowledge.

Thus, because they made the effort, Mother Earth fulfilled the desires of all her children. Prithu was so pleased with her that he embraced her and called her his daughter. That is why she is also known as *Prithvi*, or the daughter of Prithu.

Prithu decided to perform a sacrifice for the good and benefit of all. To this sacrifice he invited all the people of the earth and the devas of the heavens. Lord Vishnu came down to bless the sacrifice. He advised Prithu thus, "The wise man does not hate or injure anyone. For he knows that it is I who reside in all beings.

"The *atman* is the ruler of the body, mind and intellect. He who knows this also knows that birth and death are for the body alone and that the *atman* is ever free and immortal. Prithu, you are a wise king. Keep your mind and senses under perfect control and, completely devoted to Me, act on in the world. Do not be deluded either by joy or by misery."

Prithu in utter devotion prostrated before the Lord and said, "Lord of my heart, I desire nothing but devotion for Thee. May my ears hear nothing but Thy praises. This is my only prayer."

Sri Vishnu then blessed Prithu and returned to Vaikuntha.

Then Prithu taught his subjects how to live rightly in this world. He said, "Dedicate yourselves entirely to Him. When a man has a sincere wish to even serve Him, his mind becomes free from all the impurities gathered in previous births. If his mind is fixed on the Lord's lotus feet, he becomes free from attachment, gains supreme knowledge and conquers death."

One day Prithu was visited by the four Sanatkumaras. They said to him, "We have come for your darshan because you are such a wise and noble king. It is a pleasure to meet you because you delight in conversation upon the nature of God. True love for Him can be developed—

By having faith and reverence.

By wanting to know the Truth.

By keeping up spiritual practices.

By keeping away from the worldly.

By learning to love solitude and quiet.

By being kind and truthful.

By controlling the senses and passions.

By studying the scriptures.

By revering the wise and the holy men, and

By constantly singing the praise and glory of God.

"In the ocean of the world, the six ferocious sharks are lust, anger, greed, pride, delusion and jealousy. But if you accept Him as your ferry-man, He will take your boat across the ocean with perfect ease."

Having thus learnt from the Sanatkumaras, Prithu started contemplating more and more upon the nature of God. He remained in the world with a pure heart, not caring for the enjoyments of kingship.

After some time he made his kingdom over to his son, Vijitasva, and retired to the solitude of the forest. Here he spent his days in meditation till at last he gave up his body and merged into the Infinite Brahman.

PURANJANA

After Vijitasva, his son became the king. This son was very fond of performing yagnas and sacrifices. The entire countryside was scattered with the blades of the *kusa* grass he used for them. He was called Pracinabarhi.

Now Narada was quite fond of Pracinabarhi and felt sorry to see him waste his time and energy in the performance of rituals. He said to him, "Son, why do you waste your time like this ? You are only acquiring more *karmas*. You are slaughtering more and more innocent creatures for your sacrifices. What do you hope to gain by all this? It will never bring you any closer to the realization of the one goal in life."

Pracinabarhi was bewildered. He looked at Narada, not knowing what he was talking about. "Holy sage, " he said, "My mind is not clear. I feel confused. I know I have been attached to worldly things. Teach me the way out of it. Show me the way to the Supreme."

Narada said, "I will tell you a story. Then you will understand everything.

"There once lived a king called Puranjana. He had a very close friend. But he did not know what he did or where he lived.

"Puranjana roamed all over the world, trying to find a city where he could live. But none would satisfy him. He wanted to live in a place where all his desires would be satisfied. At last he came across a beautiful city to the south of the Himalayas. The city had stately palaces, beautiful gardens and cool, clear lakes. It had nine gates. Puranjana loved the city at once. He thought, 'Ah! This is the right place for me."

"Some time, soon after, he met a beautiful young lady strolling in the gardens with her companions and attendants. Puranjana asked her to marry him. She said to him, "I am the princess of this land. If you will be the king, I will willingly be your queen. All my attendants shall be your attendants. Live here and enjoy."

"Puranjana married her and became very attached to her indeed. So much so that if she wept, he wept; if she laughed, he laughed; if she saw, he saw; if she heard, he heard. Thus slowly, little by little, he came to lose his independence.

"For many years he lived thus, a slave to his wife. He found that he could enjoy ~nself through the nine city gates. But never was he completely satisfied. His pleasures always small and fleeting. He never got any lasting comfort or happiness.

"One day the city was attacked and stormed by King Fear. It was completely destroyed. Puranjana was driven out of it. He went out, knocking about like a madman, with no other thought in his mind but that of his beautiful wife. Thus he spent his last days.

"Then in his next birth, he was born as a lovely young girl, who married a king called Malayadhvaja. She loved her husband very much. One day, however, she found him cold in death. She could not bear to live without him. Weeping constantly, she prepared to burn herself on her husband's funeral pyre.

"At that moment, a kindly old Brahmin walked up to her and said, "O my friend, what have you come to ? Have you forgotten me, your own dear friend? You deserted me and left me in search of small enjoyments and pleasures. You became attached to a woman and lost your sense of independence. You got caught in this web of *maya*. But do you not realize that you are *not* the wife of the dead man ? *Nor* were you the husband before ? That you are neither man nor woman ? That you are my own Self – the one eternal Reality? Arise. Shed your weaknesses. Awake to this Truth."

Pracinabarhi then requested Narada to explain the story to him. So Narada continued, "Puranjana in the story stands for Purusha, the Self. The one friend he has, is Brahman, the Lord. Verily, nobody knows what He does or where He lives.

"Now the Purusha goes in search of a place to dwell in, where the maximum number of his desires can be satisfied. He looks around but finds none to his satisfaction, till at last he finds the city of nine gates, the human body. This he enters and starts enjoying himself. The wife he finds, is the intellect. United with it, he enjoys the world and the worldly things. Identifying completely with this intellect or ego, he forgets his own divine nature and becomes full of ignorance and vanity.

"The attacking general is the all-destroying Time, using disease and death as his weapons. These ultimately destroy the body.

"Once man forgets his divine nature and runs after the fleeting pleasures of the world, he becomes bound by his deeds. His deeds decide his future births.

"And when he regains his previous knowledge, when he realizes that he is none other than the Eternal Brahman, only then does he become free of *karma*.

"Therefore, devote yourself to your One Friend. For He is but you. Love Him and be free."

Pracinabarhi followed Narada's teachings. He gave his kingdom to his sons and retired to Kapilashrama at the mouth of the Ganges to practise this way of Truth. He lived in solitude and came to realise Brahman as his own true Self.

Pracinabarhi was sincere. He learnt at the feet of his master. He practised what he was taught. He came close to God. He became one with Him.

PRIYAVRATA

Priyavrata was the second son of Manu. At an early age he had learnt the spiritual truths at the feet of his master, Narada. Now he was ready to renounce the world and take Sannyasa. Manu wanted him to remain in the world and live as a royal king, ruling the earth. But Priyavrata would not listen to him.

One day Narada and Priyavrata were sitting and discussing the sacred truths. The teacher and the taught were both enjoying the divine beauty of the discourse. At this time Brahma appeared before them. They felt the presence of a heavenly being and stood up to receive him.

Brahma was pleased and smiled lovingly at them. To Priyavrata he said, "Learn to surrender yourself to the Divine Will. Your father Manu, your teacher Narada and I— all of us obey the Divine Will. A human being must go through birth and death, pleasure and pain, happiness and misery.

"As a man after a bad dream wakes up and remembers it, but is not attached to it, so too a free soul is unattached to his *karmas*.

"A man may run away from the world and its attractions, but if his mind is obsessed with passions, they will follow him wherever he goes. But if a man is devoted to God he remains in the world with a pure heart. It is my wish that you should live on and rule the land as a king keeping your mind free from passions and desires."

Priyavrata accepted this as a command. After some years he took a wife. She gave birth to ten sons and a daughter. Priyavrata ruled the land zealously and in later life, under the guidance of his teacher, Narada, took the vows of Sannyasa. His heart's dearest wish was fulfilled and he was united with God.

THE ROYAL SAGE, RISHABHA

Rishabha was a descendant of Priyavrata. He was born to his virtuous parents after they had offered many prayers to Sri Vishnu. Rishabha was himself an *avatara* of Vishnu.

Rishabha grew up to be a lovable, gifted and self-controlled young man. He studied under a preceptor and later married Jayanti, one of Indra's daughters. Rishabha had great control over his body and his mind.

Gradually, as knowledge grew within him that there is but one God in all beings and things, he came to look upon all with an equal eye. Therefore it was natural for everyone, whether high or low, rich or poor, to love him.

Rishabha was a *jivan-mukta*, and with his mind free and his heart pure, he engaged in activities for the welfare of his subjects. He was the friend of all beings. He sympathised with them and was kind and loving to all. His rule was a happy one. There was peace and contentment everywhere. He taught his sons to be not only good kings but also men of truth and perfection.

He said, "One must have a body to live in this world, but it must not be given up, to sensuous delights and pleasures which can be had even by the dogs and the pigs. It must be used wisely, as an instrument to serve the *jiva* residing in it. It must be used by man to practise *tapas* which is the highest activity for him."

Having taught them the philosophy of right living, he handed over his kingdom to his eldest son, Bharata, and went to a place outside his kingdom where he was not known. There he took the vow of *Ajagara* – staying in one place, eating whatever food came his way. Slowly, as he advanced in his *tapas*, *Siddhis** started manifesting in him. But he ignored them. Deeper and deeper he went into meditation till at last he was merged with the blessed Lord. Then one day, the tops of the bamboo forest where he was living, caught fire, and in the surrounding flames, he gave up his body.

Kings such as these have been the salt of the earth. And they were all the glorious children of this country!

KING BHARATA

It was the custom in ancient India that when a man had got his daughters married and his sons well-established in life, he would retire to the forest to spend the rest of his life in prayer and meditation. This was the duty of every man, whether he was a priest, king, merchant or labourer.

Bharata was a mighty monarch of his time. So when he had done his duty by his people, his children and his country, he left his palace, gave up his wealth and power and withdrew into the forest. One morning the people in the palace woke up to find that the king was not there. This meant that he had donned the robes of a mendicant. Bharata's son was placed on the throne and life went on as normal.

King Bharata went to the banks of the river Gandaki. He built himself a small hut of reeds thatched with leaves. He chose for his meditation the most sacred *Gayatri Mantra*. Thus passed many days, months and years. And Bharata enjoyed perfect peace and tranquillity within his heart.

One early morning, the sun was slowly rising over the horizon. Bharata had just bathed in the river. He had offered the last oblations to the rising sun, and, clad in deer-skin, he was preparing for his meditation.

A doe which had strayed from a herd of deer, felt thirsty and came to the river to quench its thirst. Just then, in a nearby jungle, a lion roared. The mother deer was with young. The lion's roar frightened her. She delivered a baby fawn in the middle of the river. Somehow she managed to get back to the bank, where, due to extreme

---

* yogic powers

shock and exertion she died almost immediately. The baby fawn, with no one to care for it, was being slowly swept down by the river current.

Bharata had watched this small drama from his hermitage. Now, seeing the urgency of the situation, he rose at once from his seat of meditation, and jumped into the river to rescue the little animal. The poor thing was cold and frightened. Gently, he carried it in his arms back to the hermitage. There he lit a fire and warmed it back to life.

This was a beautiful act, was it not? But alas! It proved to be the spiritual downfall of Bharata. He now became very fond of his deer-child. He looked after it with paternal care, fed it soft green grass and juicy fruits till it grew up to be a beautiful deer. Now it so happened that instead of turning more and more towards God, his mind turned more and more towards his deer. In the evening, when he should have been meditating upon the Lord, he would anxiously be waiting for the deer to come back from its rompings in the forest. He would sit at the door of his hermitage, in deep concern, and wonder, "O why has my little one not come home yet? Is it in trouble? Has a tiger attacked it and eaten it up?"

Thus passed some years. The noble king who had given up wealth and power, nay, the rule of an entire country; who had made his mind pure and free from attachments, had now become so attached to a little deer rescued from a running stream, that he had completely stopped his devotional practices! The more fond he grew of the deer, the less did he think of God.

The time came for Bharata to die. As he lay then, waiting for death, the deer stood by his side like a faithful son, shedding tears of sorrow. Bharata was so touched by this, that his last thought, instead of being of God, was of the deer.

Now we have always been told that a man's last thought determines his future life. So Bharata was born again as a deer. But he was born with a memory of his past life, because no devotion or prayers can ever go waste. But being in an animal body, he could not speak. He left his deer family in the hills and came to the Pulaha ashrama on the banks of the Gandaki. Here he would listen to the talks of the Rishis, hear the readings of the Upanishads and eat the remains of the offerings. And he would patiently wait for the time when he could give up his deer body because it made meditation impossible for him.

After his deer birth, Bharata was re-born as the youngest son in the family of a wealthy Brahmin. This Brahmin was a very good man. Bharata had not forgotten the experiences of his two previous births. He still remembered the pains and pangs caused by attachment. So in this life he would not even talk. He shunned *sanga** of any kind. People soon took him to be a mad man. His father and mother, however, treated him like a normal child. But soon enough, they died and left him to the care of his elder brothers and their wives.

* company

The brothers, sad to say, did not take very good care of him. They made him do all the heavy work and their wives too, treated him very unkindly. They would not even give him enough food or clothing. But Bharata uttered not a word in protest or anger. He would obey them and with perfect peace and quiet of mind he would do the work allotted to him – whether it was fetching and carrying, or ploughing the fields. Sometimes, when they lost their temper with him, he would go and sit under a tree till their anger had cooled off. Then he would go back to the house.

A robber-chief once wanted to offer a sacrifice to the goddess Bhadrakali, as he wanted to be blessed with a son. But it so happened that the victim whom they had got (because it was a human sacrifice) untied himself and ran away. The band of robbers looked high and low for him but all in vain.

After much searching, they came across the insane-looking Bharata sitting under a tree, watching and keeping guard over a field. They caught him and took him to their chief, who was pleased to see such a strong-looking man as a victim for the sacrifice. The robbers then bathed Bharata in fragrant waters, gave him new clothes, gold ornaments, sandalwood paste, flower garlands, and fed him a good meal. Then they took him and tied him to a post.

The fires were lit and as the *mantras* were being chanted, the chieftain drew out his sword and raised it to cut off Bharata's head. Bhadrakali, the goddess, could bear this no longer. In her fury she emerged out of her statue and snatched away the weapon from the hand of the chief. Then, still trembling with rage, she chopped off his head as well as the heads of all his kinsmen. Then she set Bharata free – Bharata whose mind was so absorbed in God that he did not even know that he had just been saved from a terrible death !

One day, it so happened that the palanquin of King Rahugana was passing by. One of the bearers of the palanquin suddenly fainted, and Bharata, who was sitting quietly under a tree, was forced to take his place. He took the pole of the palanquin and placed it on his shoulder, but his step was unsteady. For his heart was full of mercy, and he walked slowly, lest he should tread upon an ant or a beetle.

Now, it must have been terribly uncomfortable to be carried in a jolting palanquin. King Rahugana looked out and saw that his new bearer, although strong and sturdy, was constantly hopping and jerking. So he called out and said, "Fool. Put down the pole and rest awhile if you are tired. Yes, rest if you are tired, though you look to me as strong as two oxen put together."

Bharata then lay down the pole. He smiled, and, for the first time in his life he opened his lips to speak. "O king," he said. "Whom do you call 'fool'? Whom do you call 'strong'? If it is this body you are addressing, then it is made of the same flesh and blood as yours. I am no mad man, king. My mind is steadily fixed upon the Lord. But this body did not want to trample poor and innocent crawling worms, therefore it went slow. The true Self never wearies, for it has nothing to do with the body. It knows no command because it is neither master nor slave. It is the same Self everywhere in the universe. Then who should command and who should obey? Realize this great truth, O king, that you too may come to know this Self."

King Rahugana was astonished to hear Bharata's words of wisdom. He got down from his palanquin and prostrated before him "full-length". "Pardon me for insulting you, O holy sage," he said. "For I did not know your greatness. I wish to learn more about this Self from you. Please teach me, for I now consider myself as your disciple."

Then Bharata sat down under a tree and Rahugana sat at his feet. "King," said Bharata, "To know one's Self is the highest knowledge, but one cannot seek it in this world of constant change.

"When the mind is associated with the three *gunas* – *sattwa*, *rajas* and *tamas*, it causes bondage and suffering. When it is free from them it brings peace and happiness, and consequently, freedom.

"One cannot attain this knowledge by studying the Vedas, nor by penance, nor by performing good deeds, but by being in the company of the pure and the holy.

"The world is like a thick, dark forest where men have lost their way. In this jungle there are robbers and bandits, who rob them of their most valuable possessions. The robbers and bandits are none other than the sense objects and their experiences which rob man of his true heritage – his own divine nature. Hungry and thirsty, man looks around for something that will satisfy him. He sees a mirage and runs towards it. But alas! how can he quench his thirst at the waters of a mirage? So round and round the forest he goes, hungry, thirsty and bruised.

"The mirage is the mirage of happiness which man is constantly chasing in this world. Chasing one fleeting happiness after another, he gets tired, but never finds the happiness he is looking for.

"Then finally, a kindly friend takes him by the hand and shows him the way out of the jungle.

"This kindly friend is the compassionate teacher. He leads man out of this forest of *samsar*, and teaches him that knocking about in the world he will never find lasting happiness. For the world has no power to give it to him. Therefore he should seek the Lord.

"Now king, cut your bonds of attachment. Embrace the world in your love for Him. You shall reach Him, Who dwells in the heart of all."

This holy land of ours has always been the land of sages and men of wisdom. For it is only here that the supreme ideals of love, service, worship and meditation are taught as the means to Self-realization. We are taught to love and serve Him, not for any material gains or benefits, but for the sake of love and service themselves. In all

Bala Bhagavatam

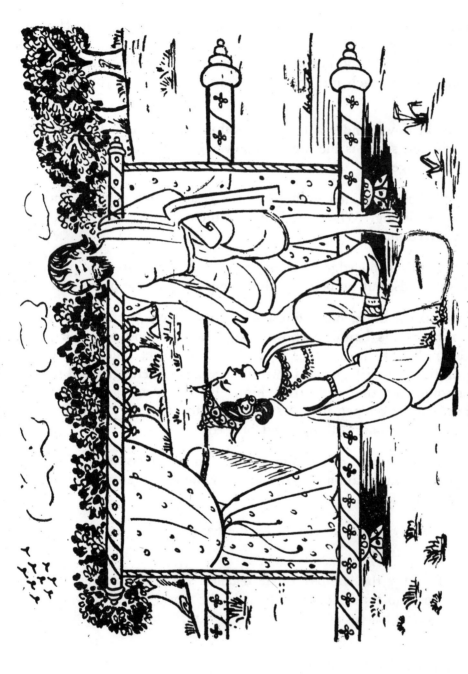

सिन्धूसौवीरपति....... त्वरया भ्रवसुः
धिरसा पादमूलं उपस्तुत: क्षमापयन् विगत –
नृपदेवस्मय उवाच ॥

(स्क 5 अ 10 श्लो 15)

Rahugana, the King of Sowveera, on the banks of Sindhu-river, immediately got down from the vehicle and fell at the feet of the Saintly-carrier, and begging for his forgiveness, and thus destroying his royal vanity,——said:

Rahugana and Bharata

these stories we see how mighty kings gave up their throne and power because of their love for Truth. They renounced all, that they may be one with God. As noble kings they dedicated themselves to the service of their subjects. As sages of the forest, they served the entire mankind.

Thus loving Him, serving Him, worshipping Him and meditating upon Him, rise to be men and women of spiritual glory and wisdom! See Him within your own hearts! Realize Him to be the very Life of every living creature!

THE STORY OF AJAMILA

Have you ever seen a crackling fire, bright and blazing? Have you noticed that no matter what you put into it, whether it be clean dry wood or dirt and filth from the roadside, it is purified and burnt down to ashes?

Similarly the name of the Lord burns the gravest of sins and reduces it to nothing. Let us see how.

This is the story of Ajamila. Ajamila was a Brahmin youth. He was honest, truthful, virtuous and modest and was well-versed in the Vedas. He was married to a good Brahmin girl and was leading a happy and contented life.

One day he went into the forest to collect flowers, fruits, sacrificial wood and the *kusa* grass for his worship. While he was returning, he saw a young woman of low birth and unclean habits. His mind was overcome with lust and passion. Forgetting his own wife and children, he went to live with this woman.

What happens when one keeps the company of the evil? One falls into degradation. Ajamila was formerly a sensible man with a pure mind. Now, in the company of his new wife, he gave up all thought of God and worship. Whatever little wealth he had, he spent on her. A time came when he did not have enough. Then he would go out and steal and cheat people and thus he managed to keep his wife and children happy.

Ajamila had ten sons by this wife. The youngest son, whom he called Narayana, was, however, his favourite. When the time came for Ajamila to die, his son was playing a little distance away from him. Suddenly, two fierce-looking messengers of Yama* appeared at his bed-side, armed with clubs and axes. They had come to drag his soul away from his body. Terrified, Ajamila shouted out for his son. "Narayana! Narayana!" he called. Thus when he called his son, Narayana, he uttered the Lord's name unconsciously. His mind dwelt upon His lotus feet.

Just then, two shining and resplendent attendants of Sri Vishnu appeared and said, "Wherefore do you propose to take him? He has meditated upon the Lord in his last moment. You have no claim on him."

---

* the god of death

Yama's messengers said, "This man, though good and virtuous in the beginning, became wicked and unholy. He led an unclean life and committed many crimes. We have a right to take him to his punishment."

But the attendants of Sri Vishnu said, "Ajamila has uttered the Lord's name with devotion. He who loves God and completely surrenders himself unto Him, is released, no matter how heavy his burden of sin! Such is the power of Narayana's name. He becomes His beloved, His very own."

Their arguments defeated, the servants of Yama left.

Ajamila was overwhelmed by the conversation of these divine beings. His heart was too full for words. Slowly, he regained his health. He left his home, wife and children and on the banks of the Ganga at Haridwara, he meditated upon the divine Lord till his hour of death. This time, he gave up his physical body and the attendants of Sri Vishnu bore him away to Vaikuntha.

INDRA AND VRITRA

Brihaspati is the teacher of the devas. The devas reside in *Swarga** and have Indra as their king. Unfortunately, Indra is not very wise. Sometimes he gives way to his anger, pride, envy, jealousy, arrogance and fear, like any human being. This often gets him into trouble.

One day, as Indra was sitting in *Swarga*, his mind got enchanted with the glamour around him and he thought, "Look at all this exquisite beauty and grandeur! And to think I am the lord of it all! Ah, I am indeed the King of kings. There is none other superior to me!" At that moment, Brihaspati, the teacher of the devas entered the court. But Indra was so puffed up with pride, that he did not rise to receive him. Now this is the greatest insult to a teacher. Brihaspati was offended by this arrogant behaviour of Indra's. Angrily, he turned on his heel and left the court. No sooner had he left than Indra realized his mistake. Quickly gathering some of his attendants with him, he went in search of the preceptor. But Brihaspati was really angry. And try as they might, Indra and his friends could not find him, for he had made himself invisible.

Now their anxiety grew. The devas and the daityas were constantly quarrelling, and any side which did not have a teacher was naturally the weaker of the two. So when the daityas came to know that the devas had offended their teacher, they attacked. And time and again, the devas suffered defeat and humiliation. At last Indra went to Brahma and asked for his help. Brahma said to him, "You are now paying the price for your arrogant folly. How could you ever forget that the teacher is placed as high as God Himself and therefore deserves all reverence and worship? But I see you have suffered enough for it. Now go to Viswarupa, the younger son of Twasta, who is a great *yogi*, and ask him to be your preceptor."

* heaven

Indra went to Viswarupa who agreed to be the teacher of the devas. He taught them the *Narayana Kavacha*, which was a prayer unto Narayana and had great potency. The devas now scored one sweeping victory after another. The asuras lost miserably. In the midst of all this, an unfortunate incident took place. Viswarupa was a daitya from his mother's side and a deva from his father's. So when he offered oblations in the sacrificial fire to the devas he secretly offered a share of it to the daityas too. But somehow Indra came to know of this. He became so angry that one day, when Viswarupa was at his worship, he came up from behind and cut off his head with a sword.

When Twastadeva heard of this, he lit a sacrificial fire, poured oblations into it, and commanded a demon to arise from it, for the destruction of Indra. An awful looking creature called Vritra rose from the flames and filled the air with his hot breath. He had a flaming tongue, which would lick anything that came its way. All the people of the three worlds fled in fear at the sight. But the devas took courage in their hands and attacked the monster from all sides. They used every weapon they could lay their hands on. But Vritra only swallowed them as if they were the most delicious fruits in the world!

The devas were terrified. They went to Sri Narayana and asked him for help. Narayana said to Indra, "Go to the Rishi Dadhichi and ask him to give you his body. Then from his bones shall issue a weapon with which you will be able to cut off Vritra's head."

So the gods went to Dadhichi and asked him to give them his body which had been strengthened by the constant repetition of the *Narayana Kavacha*. Dadhichi, large-hearted sage that he was, gave it to them. The devas then extracted the divine weapon from the bones of his arms. Confident of victory, they attacked Vritra who had on his side the entire host of daityas and asuras. The devas wiped them out completely, till at last, there was only Vritra, standing all by himself, facing the devas. But he was undaunted. For he had only to open his mouth and roar and hundreds of devas would fall down unconscious. And he would trample upon them as an elephant would over a lotus bed. Indra was astonished at the strength and skill of his enemy. He hurled at him the special weapon. But Vritra picked it up and hurled it at Indra's own elephant, who fell down unconscious. Then Indra got down to fight with Vritra, face to face. Vritra, when he saw the slayer of his brother, was filled with rage. Trembling with emotion, he said, "I am extremely happy that I now have you in front of me, so that I may pierce your cruel heart with my trident. You shamelessly killed my brother, who was your own Guru. Even the rakshasas condemn you for this deed of yours."

"I am also fully aware that the weapon you carry in your hands has been got from the bones of Maharshi Dadhichi, and that this sacred weapon shall kill me. Now go ahead and do your job. I am but waiting to be released from this body of mine that I may merge myself with Lord Narayana, that I may tread the path of yoga and ever be His devotee."

इन्द्रशत्रो विवर्धस्व मा चिरं जहि विद्विषम् ।
अथान्वाहार्यंपचनादुत्थितो घोरदर्शनः ।।
कृतान्त इव लोकानां युगान्तसमये यथा।
             (स्क. 6 अ. 9 श्लो. 12/13)

"Oh! Enemy of Indra, manifest; let us not wait for long in routing the enemy.........Then from the sacrificial fire rose the terrible–looking monster-form of Vritra, to destroy the world....... as though the end of the world had come".

Vritra springs from Sacrificial Fire

Then he turned his mind to the Lord and fervently prayed. "My heart yearns for the sight of You, O Lord! Grant my prayer that I may be united with You in every thought, word and deed. I desire nothing else in this great, big, universe of Yours."

Vritra gave a mighty roar and hurled his flaming trident at Indra. Indra destroyed it mid-way with his divine weapon, and also cut off the arm that hurled it. Vritra, enraged, lifted up his iron club and brought the weapon down to earth. All those who were present praised this feat of his. Indra looked embarrassed. But Vritra encouraged him to pick it up again and use it against him. Indra was now dumb with amazement at the nobility of his enemy. He said to him, "O chief of the asuras. You are indeed the noblest of all creatures. You have attained eternal *bhakti* for the Lord and have indeed gone beyond His *maya*. Hail to you.!"

He picked up the weapon and cut off the other arm of the demon. Vritra now opened wide his mouth and swallowed both Indra and his elephant, Airavata. The gods and the demons who were watching the gruesome battle thought that this was the end of Indra. But Indra still had the sacred weapon with him, and so he tore open Vritra's belly from inside and came out triumphant. Then there was the sound of a crashing thunderbolt as he chopped off Vritra's head, which bounced and rolled away and then lay still.

Now the most amazing thing happened. Open-mouthed as the devas watched, the soul of Vritra entered straight into Sri Narayana, who was standing amidst them all. Vritra's prayer had been answered !

Why should Vritra have been favoured thus, by the divine mercy of the Lord ? Listen.

CHITRAKETU

Chitraketu was the king of Surasena. He had everything that a monarch could wish for. Rich lands, good ministers, obedient subjects, youthful vigour and a thousand beautiful wives. But he had no son. And this made him very unhappy.

One day the sage Angiras visited his royal court and found the king sad and thoughtful. "King," he said, "There is something which is worrying you beyond measure. This can only be due to some unfulfilled desire."

"You know everything in my heart, O revered sage! I have all that a man could possibly wish for, to make him happy. But I have not got the fondest desire of my heart granted yet. I have no son."

Angiras then blessed him and his chief queen and said, "This too, you shall have, O king. But your son will not only bring you much happiness, but much sorrow also."

In course of time, a son was born to the chief queen. There was great rejoicing throughout the country. The king, like a generous rain-bearing cloud, showered rich gifts on his courtiers and citizens. The happiness of the king and queen knew no bounds.

They doted upon the little baby, who was the very joy of their lives. Now the other queens grew jealous. So one day they poisoned the baby prince. When the nurse went to fetch him, she saw his eyes turned upward in death. It was terrible to see the deep sorrow of the king and the queen. Their grief was inconsolable. The king would beat his chest and lament loudly his loss.

The sage Angira and the divine seer Narada now appeared before him and said, "Whom do you weep for, O king? Who was there before your son was born and who is there now that he is no more? The soul is but one. It is the body which is different. Why be attached to a body, king, when you know its perishable nature?"

Chitraketu wiped his tears of grief, and said, "Holy sages. Shed your light of wisdom upon me that my ignorance may vanish. Teach me the ways of the Lord."

Angira and Narada taught him the paths of worship and meditation. Chitraketu learnt much at their feet and then fixed his mind in meditation upon the Lord. Soon, Bhagavan gave him darshan and blessed him. Chitraketu then retired to the valleys of Mount Meru, and spent his time in devotional practices.

One day, he was passing Mount Kailash in his aerial chariot. There he saw all the sages of the land gathered around the feet of Lord Shiva. Shiva was teaching them and Parvati was seated on his lap. When Chitraketu saw them, he passed a rude remark, which was heard by the divine couple. Now Shiva is ever calm and controlled. He just smiled and went on teaching. But Parvati felt insulted. In her anger, she cursed Chitraketu and said, "To redeem yourself of this sin, you will have to take an asura birth."

Chitraketu, with good grace, accepted the curse.

So when Twastadeva demanded that a demon should arise from the sacrificial fire to kill Indra, Chitraketu sprang up as Vritra, the fiercest of them all. He had always been a devotee of Hari (*Hari Bhakta*), so even in his demon-body, which he had acquired to fulfil the curse, he retained instinctively an unceasing devotion for the Lord. When he died, therefore, where else should he have gone but to Narayana?

HIRANYAKASIPU

Hiranyaksha and Hiranyakasipu were two demon brothers. We already know the story of the end of Hiranyaksha.

Hiranyakasipu consoled his brother's wife and his other relatives with words of wisdom and said, "Do not mistake the body for the Self. So long as my brother acted through his body, you mistook it to be him as you are now mistaking his dead and lifeless form to be him. In fact it is not so. The wise know that the body is perishable and that the soul is nothing but imperishable."

But although Hiranyakasipu spoke these words of great wisdom, he, in his heart, swore enmity to Sri Vishnu, and vowed to avenge the death of his brother. He went to the Mount Mandara, and there steadily performed the most rigorous *tapas*. His body became covered with ant-hills and wild grass and his flesh was eaten away by worms. The force of his *tapas* was so great that the very earth rocked. The planets moved out of their orbits and changed their positions. The waters of the oceans rose high. Mountains toppled over. And many places just caught fire! Unable to bear the heat any longer, the devas went to Brahma and pleaded with him to save them from the disaster that was brewing. Then Brahma went to the asura's ashrama and was wonder-struck at the greatness of his penance. He took some water from his *kamandalu*, and sprinkling it on Hiranyakasipu, asked him what boon he wanted.

The demon's body became whole and youthful and shone with the brilliance of molten gold. He prostrated before Brahma, and said, "Lord, grant me this boon: let me not die at the hands of any being created by you, nor at the hands of any being not created by you, be it god, man, demon, animal or even an inanimate thing. Let it not be by day or by night, outdoors or indoors, in the sky or on the earth; let it not be by any weapon whatsoever. Grant me also complete sovereignty such as you enjoy in the worlds of men, demons and gods, and all the *siddhis* that are acquired after the most rigorous penance and mind-control."

"So be it – "*Tathaastu!*" granted Brahma, the Creator of the Universe.

On the strength of this boon, Hiranyakasipu conquered the threee worlds and became their supreme overlord. In his kingdom, sacrifices were no longer offered to God but only to him. He made people say prayers to him, and he disregarded the commands of all the scriptures. There was immense material prosperity, but people were fed up with his reign of terror. They prayed to Lord Vishnu to help them. To them He addressed words of consolation, "Do not worry. I shall destroy this rakshasa Myself, in spite of the boon he has got from Brahma."

And this is how it came about.

PRAHLADA

Hiranyakasipu had four sons of whom the youngest was called Prahlada. From birth itself, he was a great devotee of Vishnu (*Hari Bhakta*). He would constantly chant the glories of Lord Vishnu, which caused great alarm to his father.

The teacher of the daityas was a learned Brahmin called Sukracharya. He had two sons who were the tutors of Prahlada. It was their duty to teach Prahlada how to be a perfect daitya. He learnt all his daitya lessons very well indeed but his heart was not in them. Whenever he got the opportunity, he would sing the glories of Sri Vishnu. This troubled his teachers very much, so they took him to the king and told him all about it. Hiranyakasipu lovingly took Prahlada on his lap and asked him what he thought was the greatest good. Prahlada replied at once, "I think that the highest good is to leave the home where one is always thinking in terms of 'I' and 'mine', and to go into the forest and undisturbed, meditate upon Sri Hari."

38

Bala Bhagavatam

श्राह्मर्षसमाविष्टः कथापिर्मुतलोचनः । १

वध्यतामश्वथ वध्यो नि: सारयत नेर्ह्लता : ॥

(स्क. 7 ऋ. 5 ख्लो. 34)

Hiranyakasipu cried: "Ha! ah!" in his terrible anger, eyes turned red. "Go and kill Prahlada", cried the king to his guards.
Prahlada and Hiranyakasipu

Sri Hari! That hated name from the mouth of his own son! Hiranyakasipu called the teachers of the boy aside and said to them, "I do not understand where he gets these ideas from. Keep a close watch over him and see that he does not come in contact with anyone who is likely to utter the name of Vishnu. Perform your duty faithfully or else there will be trouble for you !"

The teachers, with great care taught him all about righteousness (*Dharma*), wealth (*Artha*) and desire-fulfilment (*Kama*) but left out even the mention of *Moksha*. Prahlada repeated all the material and secular lessons after them very faithfully. Then they took him before the king once more, and asked him to repeat the lesson he had just learnt. Instead, Prahlada said, "Devotion to Lord Vishnu – hearing His glories, reciting them, constantly remembering Him, attending upon Him, worshipping Him, adoring Him, serving Him, being His friend, and surrendering oneself entirely to Him– these are the nine-fold modes of devotion (*Bhakti*) which must be practised at all times."

*श्रवणं कीर्तनं विष्णो: स्मरणं पादसेवनम् ।
अर्चनं वन्दनं दास्यं सख्यमात्मनिवेदनम् ॥१॥
इति पुंसर्पिता विष्णौ भक्तिश्चेन्नवलक्षणा ।
क्रियते भगवत्यद्धा तन्मन्येऽधीतमुत्तमम् ॥२॥

Now Hiranyakasipu was really furious. He abused the teachers and called them 'vile Brahmins', then turned his angry red eyes on the little Prahlada. The king fretted and fumed and said, "Tell me the truth. Who has taught you all this nonsense about Vishnu? You can be no son of mine, you vile creature, if you keep singing the praises of your own father's enemy."

Prahlada said, "They are indeed blind who have no thought for Narayana, but who, derive the same cheap pleasures from the same sense objects, birth after birth. They are like the oxen which go round and round, tied by the same rope. It is Sri Narayana alone who can lift one out of this."

Hiranyakasipu's moustache bristled with rage. His fury knew no bounds. His chest heaved and his breath came faster. He pursed his lips together, and then suddenly he shouted and his voice was like that of a thunderclap. 'Take that child away! Put him to death ! Let me never see him again!!"

The wicked blood-thirsty asuras pounced upon the child, Prahlada, with cries of, "Kill him! Kill him!" And they pierced the little boy with their pointed and poison-tipped spears. But nothing happened to Prahlada, for his mind was concentrated upon the Lord, and the brave boy did not even feel the spear thrusts!

* 1. Listening to His glories; 2. Loudly declaring them (in your actions and speech) 3. Constantly remembering Sri Vishnu; 4. Serving Him (by serving the needy and the hungry among His creatures); 5. Worshipping Him (by bringing joy into the hearts of others around you); 6. Adoring Him; 7. Serving Him as His slave; 8. Befriending Him; 9. Surrender-totally unto His grace and love – these are the nine ways of devotion. One who practises them, does everything for the Lord, and I consider he has learnt his lessons well.

Hiranyakasipu was now at his wits' end. How could such a thing happen? This was strange indeed! And he was frightened, too. For he felt very strongly that he would meet his end because of this boy. But all the devilish passions of a daitya were now aroused in him, and he tried various means of putting Prahlada to death. He ordered him to be trampled upon by a mad elephant. The enraged animal rushed on to the little boy, but stopped short of him, bowed his head and turned away! Then Hiranyakasipu ordered the daityas to take him to the top of the highest mountain and drop him from it. Prahlada was all the time thinking of Sri Narayana, with the result he came down as gentle as a flower is brought down by the breeze on the grass! His food was poisoned. He was bitten by poisonous snakes. He was locked up in a solitary cell for days without food. He was thrown into the sea. He was burnt by fire. He was made the object of numerous magical spells and enchantments. But he always came out of them safe and sound! This is the grace of the Lord – *Narayana-Kripa.*

Hiranyakasipu was now thoroughly frustrated. This was the first time that his authority had been challenged. Besides it was also a tremendous blow to his pride. For up till now he had never known fear, failure or humiliation. The teachers tried to pacify him by saying that Prahlada was still too small to know what he was saying and that in time he would learn to behave like a true daitya.

So once again, Prahlada was given to the care of his teachers who taught him the duties of a true king. They taught him the asuric sciences all over again. One day, when the teachers were away, Prahlada got together the other little daitya boys and taught them how to chant the name of the Lord. He said, "O young daityas. Do not follow the example of your elders. They are given to the pleasures of their senses. Devote your hearts to Sri Narayana. Learn to love all living creatures because they are His very own. Be kind and compassionate to all.

*कौमारे आचरेत् प्राज्ञो धर्मान् भागवतानिह ।
दुर्लभं मानुषं जन्म तदप्य ध्रुवमर्थदम् ॥१॥
यथा हि पुरुषस्येह विष्णोः पादोपसर्पणम् ।
यदेष सर्वभूतानां प्रिय आत्मेश्वरः सुहृत् ॥२॥
तस्मात्सर्वेषु दयां कुरुत सौहृदम् ।
आसुरं भावसुन्मुच्य यया तुष्यत्यधोक्षजः ॥३॥

The little daityas liked what he told them. So they all sat down together and sang the glories of the Lord, as taught to them by Prahlada.

---

*1.   In this human life, a wise man should practise virtues conducive to God-realization in his very childhood; for the birth of a human being alone can bring us to our goal, and such a birth is obtained with great difficulty; it is fleeting too.

2.   The only course advisable to a person in this world is to betake himself to the Feet of Lord Vishnu; for He is the Ruler and the Beloved Friend, nay, the very Self of all created beings.

3.   Therefore by giving up the demoniac disposition, show compassion and love to all beings, whereby Lord Vishnu, who is beyond sense-perception, will be pleased.

Hiranyakasipu soon came to hear about this. He ordered Prahlada to be brought before him. "Fool," he said, "You seem to be bent upon creating trouble in your own race. Time and again you defy my authority without the least fear in your heart. Do you not know that I am the lord of the three worlds and that I shall put you to death at once? Though where you get this extraordinary strength to resist me, I cannot imagine."

Humbly, Prahlada folded his palms before his father and said, "Father, my only strength is Sri Vishnu. He is not only my strength, but also yours. He is the strength of the whole universe."

"Wretch!" screamed Hiranyakasipu. "Again Vishnu! There is no Vishnu. I am the only Bhagavan, the only Ishwara."

"No, father," said Prahlada. "Sri Vishnu alone is the Lord of the Universe. He is without beginning and without end. He is present in the entire universe and, therefore, He alone is to be worshipped."

"Fool! Is your Vishnu present in this pillar too?"

"Yes, in that too," said Prahlada.

"Then let Him show Himself to me," said Hiranyakasipu, cutting down the pillar in uncontrolled rage.

Wonderful, this prayer of the daitya king! It was heard!!

For, suddenly the pillar split into two with such tremendous force that the sound echoed in all the worlds and filled man, god, animal and demon with fear. They all trembled violently, for they thought the world would now come to an end.

And out of the pillar came a mighty Being, half-man-half-lion (Nara-Simham). He was of a huge build and his stature was awe-inspring. His face, eyes, and mane had a brilliance that shed their dazzling light all around. His neck was short and thick. His chest was broad and mighty. His tongue had an edge as sharp as a razor's and his teeth and claws were sharp and glistening. He was the man-lion-*avatara* of Lord Vishnu! All the daityas present, though they were armed with the most dangerous weapons, fled in sheer fright. Hiranyakasipu lifted his iron mace to strike him. But the Narasimha roared a tremendous roar which was at once like a man's laughter and a lion's roar. With the greatest ease, he picked up the mighty daitya and placed him in his lap across his thighs. Then, with another of his heart-rending laughs, he tore open the heart and bowels of Hiranyakasipu and flung the dead carcass aside. Then he turned his countless arms on all sides and slew the wicked supporters of the dead king. And with one leap, he seated himself on the throne.

Flowers were showered on him from above. Brahma, Shiva, the Rishis, the gods and the goddesses, all sang the praises of Sri Vishnu. There was great rejoicing in the three worlds. But Narasimha continued to quiver and none of the gods or Rishis dared

सत्यं विधातुं निजभृत्य भाषितं
व्याप्तिं च भूतेष्वखिलेषु चात्मनः ।
अदृश्यतात्यद्भुतरूपमुद्वहन्
स्तंभे सभायां न मृगं न मानुषम् ॥

....

.........ददार लीलया नखैः ।   (स्क. 7 अ. 8 श्लो. 18, 29)

To fulfil the words of His devotee (Prahlad) and to prove His own all-pervasiveness, He emerged out from the smashed pillar in the Darbar Hall in the form of a man-lion. This man-lion tore the king with his claws and killed him, as though in play.
Narasimha Avatara

approach him. Brahma then sent Prahlada to him. He approached Him slowly, and prostrated before him "full length". The Lord, in an outpouring of divine love, placed His hand on the head of His little devotee, and raised him to his feet. Prahlada felt a thrill of joy and his frail body shook with the ecstasy of his feeling. A spontaneous prayer burst forth from his lips and he praised the Lord in many loving words.

And the Lord said, "Prahlada, My loving child. Ask from Me any boon you wish for." Prahlada shook his head and said, "My Lord. Do not tempt me. to ask You for earthly or heavenly boons. I have seen Your divine countenance. I desire nothing else." But Narayana said, "Nay, my son. Ask something." So Prahlada asked his boon, "Lord, let me not have any desires that will drive me away from my love for You. I desire nothing but intense and everlasting love for Your feet."

And the Lord blessed him, "You have asked Me for no reward. Yet it is My wish that you should rule as a king and enjoy the splendour and blessings of a kingdom. I know you would wish freedom for your father. Understand that he was purified the moment I touched him. Now perform his last rites and rule the land till the end of this cycle. You shall then come to Me and attain My own Being."

Prahlada bowed his head in obedience to the Will of the Lord.

Let this *Bhakti* of the little daitya boy find its echo in every corner of this land! Let his example be followed by every little boy and girl. Let his prayers resound in every heart. Let him lead us all to the vision of the Lord!

GAJENDRA MOKSHA

An elephant king once resided in a forest on Mount Trikoota. There were many beautiful rivers and lakes, the waters of which were always fresh and sweet. Tiny sparkling gems lay scattered on the banks of the rivulets. Celestial trees and plants grew in a garden in the forest. They bore the loveliest flowers and the juiciest fruits. The garden belonged to Varuna, the god of oceans, and because of its exquisite charm and beauty, the apsaras often used it as their play-ground.

One day, the elephant king, whose name was Gajendra, entered the garden with his entire family. It was hot and Gajendra felt his head reel. So he entered one of the cool lakes to refresh himself. He quenched his thirst and passed on some water to others of his herd. Just then, he felt his feet attacked by a powerful crocodile. It started dragging him into the water, and he struggled hard to free himself from the clutches of the vicious animal. All the other elephants screamed and shrieked. They trumpeted loudly and tried to pull their leader out of the water. But none of their efforts could help poor Gajendra. He fought with the crocodile for a long long time. He tried every means of escape, but they all failed miserably. At last, spent and exhausted, he felt his last moment drawing near. Death was at his door. He turned his thoughts to the Lord and prayed ardently to Him for help.

Sri Hari heard the desperate cry of the royal elephant. He mounted his Garuda and with all the devas, went to help Gajendra. He pulled the crocodile out of the water and split open its mouth with His divine *chakra*. Gajendra was at last free from the many torments he had suffered when he was at the mercy of the crocodile.*

+ मन्ये धनाभिजनरुपतपः श्रुतौजस्तेजः
   प्रभावबलपौरूष बुद्धि योगाः ।
   नाराघनाय हि भवन्ति परस्य पुंसो
   भक्त्या तुतोष भगवान् गजयूथपाय ॥

The crocodile was actually a gandharva called Huhu. One day he was bathing in a tank. The Rishi Devala also went there to bathe. Huhu tried to play tricks on the Rishi. Devala cursed him, saying that he would turn into a crocodile. He was released from the curse by the touch of the Lord's divine discus, and he regained his gandharva-form.

In his previous birth, Gajendra was Indradyumna, a Pandya king. He was a great devotee of Sri Hari. He took the vow of silence, and sat in the mountains, deep in meditation. Rishi Agastya along with his disciples came to his ashrama. But the king did not rise to receive them, because he was lost in meditation. Agastya cursed him.** "You who appear to be dull-witted like an elephant, be you an elephant yourself! And so Indradyumna, the Pandya king, became Gajendra, the elephant king. But even though Gajendra was an elephant, he retained, to some extent, his devotion to the Lord from his previous birth. This he remembered when he was absolutely desparate and saw no other means of escape from the clutches of the crocodile.

---

* Each individual *jiva* in this world is like Gajendra – forgetful of the Lord, extremely attached to the family. To cool off his desires for sense-enjoyments, he plunges straightaway into the pleasures of the world. Before he even knows it, he is caught up in the net of samsar from which he cannot escape. It is then, by Lord's grace, he remembers the one Lord Who will never forsake him in his hour of need. He appeals to Him piteously, and Bhagavan, in His infinite kindness, rushes to the rescue of His sincere devotee.

+ I think that more than wealth, high birth, beauty, austerit. learning, power, intelligence and yoga, it is *Bhakti* which is most suitable for the worship of the Lord. The elephant king pleased Bhagawan by his *Bhakti*.

** Wherever we come across Rishis cursing apparently innocent individuals, we may think it unjust or unfair. But before we rashly condemn the Rishis as given to frequent and unnecessary bouts of anger, let us examine the reasons for them. So far we have seen how Jaya and Vijaya were cursed by the four Sanatkumaras, Diti was cursed by Kasyapa, Indradyumna was cursed by Agastya, even Parikshit was cursed by Sringi.

1) The curses illustrate the law of *Karma* – that without a cause no effect is possible; that people will have to enjoy or suffer the fruits of their past actions. Jaya and Vijaya had asuric instincts, which could not be seen because of the *sattwic* atmosphere of Vaikuntha where they lived. Their incarnations as Hiranyakasipu and Ravana helped them to exhaust these baser instincts, so that they could return to Vaikuntha, purer in spirit.

Diti gave birth to two asuric sons, no doubt, but she had her salvation through her grand-son, Prahlada. Similarly, although Indradyumna was cursed into being an elephant, he was saved by the Lord Himself Who carried him to Vaikuntha with Him.

2) The curses indicate the power of thought once the mind has become fully *sattwic*.

3) They also show that mighty sages, in their total surrender to the Lord, have become instruments of His will in punishing the wrong. And in all such punishments, not only are the individuals chastened but the entire world is reorganised.

But for Jaya and Vijaya, the world would have been less educated, less evolved.

THE CHURNING OF THE MILKY OCEAN

One day the Rishi Durvasa was returning from Vaikuntha. He had been on a visit to Sri Vishnu. On the way, he met Indra. Durvasa presented him with a flower garland which had been given to him by Sri Vishnu. But Indra was in a proud and arrogant mood. He took the garland and put it around the neck of his elephant. The elephant threw the garland on the ground and trampled upon it. This enraged Durvasa. It was an insult, not only to him but also to his beloved Lord Vishnu. Durvasa cursed Indra and said, "You have become proud because of your riches and wealth. I curse you and the three worlds you rule. They shall lose their prosperity and glory."

This curse took effect immediately. Indra, pale, drawn, and lustreless went to Brahma on Mount Meru. Brahma saw that the heavens and the earth had lost all their glory and splendour. All religious practices had been stopped. The gods had become weak and the asuras had become strong and powerful. With the result, more and more devas were losing their lives day by day, and the asuras seemed to gather more and more life and energy. Brahma did not know what to do. So Brahma, Indra and some other devas went to Sri Vishnu, and asked Him to help them.

To the distressed devas, the Lord said, "The asuras are now powerful. Since they are the stronger side, make peace with them. Ask their help in churning the Milky Ocean. As a result of this *amrita* shall come out, drinking which you shall all become immortal. Throw all the plants, herbs and creepers into the ocean. Make Mount Mandara your churning-rod and Vasuki, the king of serpents as your churning-rope. Be kind and courteous to the asuras. They will help you to churn the ocean. If they put before you terms and conditions, accept them gracefully. From the churning of the ocean deadly poison called Halahala shall arise. But do not be afraid of it. Many other things will also issue out as a result of the churning. But do not express any anger, greed or desire for them. Be diligent, watchful and careful and I shall help you." And then Lord Vishnu disappeared.

So Indra and the devas went to Bali, the king of the asuras, and explained to him Sri Vishnu's plan for churning the ocean. Bali was a wise and clever commander and he knew that this was not the time to fight but to make peace. So he agreed to the plans of the devas. The devas and the asuras then went to the Mount Mandara and uprooted the golden mountain. They carried it to the ocean. Vasuki, the serpent king, agreed to be the rope provided he got a share of the *amrita*. This the devas promised him.

At last the churning started. The devas, headed by Sri Vishnu, caught the serpent's head and the asuras caught the tail. But then the asuras said to Vishnu, "Do not try to cheat us. The *Shasras* tell us that it is inauspicious to hold the tail of a serpent." So Vishnu smiled at them and handed them the mouth end of the snake. The devas went to the tail end.

Although the churning had started, the mountain proved to be too heavy for the joint strength of the devas and the asuras. It quickly sank to the bottom of the ocean.

ततश्चाविरभूत्साक्षाच्छी रमा भगवत्परा ।
रञ्जयन्ती दिशः कान्या विद्युत्सौदामनी यथा । (स्क.8 अ.8 श्लो. 8)

Then rose Rema, Lakshmi, the Supreme Lady of Auspiciousness, blinding the four quarters with Her radiance divine.

Lakshmi rising from the Milky Ocean

Now they did not know what to do. Sri Vishnu assumed the form of a Giant Tortoise. He dived to the bottom of the ocean and lifted it up on His back.

As the churning continued, fire and smoke came out of the thousand mouths of Vasuki. The devas and the asuras started suffocating. Vishnu revived the devas by sending down clouds, rain, and wind. The pollution was removed.

The first thing that came out of the ocean was a most dangerous poison. Its fumes rose into the air and spread on all sides. The animals of the sea, land and sky became choked by it and they, in sheer terror took refuge at the feet of Shiva. Shiva gathered all the poison in the palm of his hand and swallowed it up. But his Consort, Mother Parvati, fearing for her Lord, quickly caught his throat with her delicate hands. The poison could not go down. Shiva would not spit it out. The poison got absorbed in his neck. This gave his throat a blue colour. That is why Lord Shiva is also known as Sri Neelakantha. A few drops of the poison fell to the ground and they were quickly swallowed by snakes, scorpions, and poisonous plants and animals.

Now that the atmosphere had been cleared of the fumes and the poison, the churning was taken up with greater vigour and energy. A sacred sacrificial vessel called Surabhi came out of the ocean, which was claimed by the Rishis. Next came the famous white horse, Uchhaishrava, which was taken by Bali, followed by Airavata, a magnificent white elephant which was taken by Indra. The Kaustubha gem, lotus-coloured and beautiful, went to adorn the chest of Sri Vishnu. After this came the Parijata tree, which fulfills all wishes, and then a group of beautiful apsaras.

But what made both gods and demons catch their breath in awe and wonder was the emergence of the goddess Lakshmi. Her splendour and brilliance filled the four quarters of the earth. There she stood, in all her shining glory, beautiful and ever-pure, with a garland of fresh lotuses in her hand! Then she went up to Sri Hari and placed it around His neck. She had accepted Him as Her husband. He placed her in His heart. Brahma, Shiva and all the other devas worshipped Her. The Brahmins chanted Vedic hymns and sprinkled on Her holy water from golden pots. Lakshmi became the Goddess of prosperity and the fortune among the devas. Verily, She is the fountain of fortune, and they, on whom she casts her benign glances, slowly acquire all the qualities of goodness and virtue.

After Lakshmi, there arose from the churning a lotus-eyed beauty called Varuni, who was the goddess of all intoxicating drinks. She was taken by the asuras.

On and on the churning continued, till at last from the ocean came up a magnificent youth, Dhanvantari, who was an *amsa** of Lord Vishnu. He carried in his hands the jar of *amrita*. When the asuras saw this, they were filled with greed. They snatched the jar from the hands of the divine youth, and even started fighting among themselves for the *amrita*. "I should get it first!" "No, not you. I shall take it first!" "Who

---

* part

are you to take it first? I should be the one to get it first!" Thus they squabbled and quarrelled among themselves. The weaker asuras became jealous and said, "This is not right. The devas have helped us to get the *amrita*. They should get a share of it too." In the midst of all this confusion, the gentle devas appealed to Sri Vishnu for help.

Lord Vishnu at once took the form of a most beautiful and enchanting young girl called Mohini. She was so lovely that at once all the asuras fell in love with her. They gave her the pot of *amrita* and asked her to distribute it to whomsoever she pleased. She looked at them sweetly and fluttered her eyelashes and said, "But are you sure you can trust me – a mere woman?" "Yes! Yes! You distribute it, please," cried the asuras in a frenzy of passion.

And Mohini said, "Ah, but you will have to put up with anything I do, whether right or wrong." The asuras agreed.

So Mohini balanced the pot of *amrita* delicately on her hip. The devas and the asuras collected in the hall after their bath. She separated them in two rows and started distributing the *amrita* among the devas first. By the time she had finished with them, the jar was empty. But it so happened that Rahu, one of the daityas, had disguised himself as a deva and had sat with them. Before he could swallow the nectar, the Sun and the Moon spotted him, and Sri Vishnu cut off his head with His *chakra*. But his head had tasted *amrita* and was therefore immortal. The Lord turned it into the planet Rahu, which causes the eclipses of the Sun and the Moon, showing his (Rahu's) eternal enmity to them.

When the *amrita* had been wholly spent, Lord Vishnu assumed His own form and left the place on the back of Garuda. The daityas suddenly woke up from their infatuation and were furious when they learnt how they had been cheated. They launched a terrible war against the devas. But the devas were immortal with Sri Vishnu on their side, so how could they possibly lose? The asuras suffered a miserable defeat. They got what they deserved, for they were constantly giving way to their lower tendencies of passion, greed, lust and anger.

VAMANA AVATARA

Bali, the king of the asuras, was the son of Virocana, and the grandson of Prahlada. He had many times been defeated by Indra in battle. Now he wanted to take revenge. His Guru, Sukracharya, advised him to perform the Viswajit Yagna. Bali received from the sacrificial fire, a golden chariot, some horses, a golden bow, two quivers with an inexhaustible supply of arrows, and a divine *kavacha* or protective armour. Armed with these, he attacked Indra, took his capital by storm and routed all the celestials. He then seized the kingdom and made himself the monarch of the three worlds, Triloki.

For this success of his, Bali performed one hundred Aswamedha yagnas as his thanks-giving to the Lord.

Now Aditi, the mother of Indra, was troubled that her son had been defeated. When her husband Kasyapa returned after a long spell of meditation in the forest, she told him of her sorrows. Kasyapa advised her to meditate upon Lord Vishnu, Who is the remover of all grief. He taught her the prayer to invoke Sri Vishnu. She prayed to the Lord with such sincerity and devotion, that He gave her His Vision-divine (darshan).*

To her, He said, "O mother of the devas. I know what is in your heart. Your desire will be fulfilled and I will soon be born as your Son."

So when the time came, the Lord was born from Aditi's womb. He was born as an adult dwarf (Vamana). All the celestials rejoiced and there was much beating of drums and blowing of trumpets. The devas and the Rishis gathered in Kasyapa's ashrama. Then the child was named Vamana, which meant 'dwarf'. There and then they performed the sacred thread ceremony of the child, and initiated him into *brahmacharya-ashrama*. The gods and goddesses presented him with all the necessary things which a *brahmachari* needs. They gave him the sacred thread, the string around the waist, a water-pot (*kamandalu*), the loin cloth, the *mala*, the tiger skin and the begging bowl. Uma, the auspicious consort of Shiva gave him his first *bhiksha*.

At this time Bali was performing an Aswamedha yagna on the banks of the river Narmada. He had invited all the Brahmins of the land. Vamana also went there. Bali and all the other priests rose to receive him, for even in his youth he glowed with spiritual beauty. Bali washed his feet with water and sprinkled his own head with the washings. Then he prostrated before him and said, "What is it that you wish, O Brahmin? I shall give you anything you ask for, be it land, gold, houses, cows or horses."

Vamana was greatly pleased by this. He said, "You are indeed the fit grandson of Prahlada. I am happy to see your love and reverence. You have performed your *dharma* well and I see you have a very charitable nature. From you I ask but three

---

*
नमस्तुभ्यं भगवते पुरूषाय महीयसे ।
सर्वंभूतनिवासाय वासुदेवाय साक्षिणे ॥१॥
नमः शिवाय रूद्राय नमः शक्तिधरायच ।
सर्वविद्याधिपतये भूतानां पतये नमः ॥२॥
नमो हिरण्यगर्भाय प्राणाय जगदात्मने ।
योगैश्वर्यशरीराय नमस्ते योग हेतवे ॥३॥
नमस्ते आदिदेवाय साक्षिभूताय ते नमः ।
नारायणाय ऋषये नराय हरये नमः ॥४॥

Salutations to the Supreme Lord!
Salutations to Him, Who is both Shiva and Shakti, Who is the Self in all beings.
Salutations to the Lord of learning, the Lord of all beings, Who is Prana, Who is the very Soul of the entire universe.
Salutations to Him Who is the Supreme Yogi, Who is the goal of all Yoga.
Salutations to Narayana, Who has no beginning, Who is the one Knower, the One-Witness (of everything in His created world).

Bala Bhagavatam

त्रिविक्रमेरिमंल्लोकान् विश्वकाय: कमिष्यति ।
सर्वंस्व विष्णवे दत्वा मूढ ! वतिष्यसे कथम् ।
(स्क. 8 अ. 19 श्लो. 33)

Sukracharya said, "By this victory of the Three-worlds, by this All-pervading One, all the Universe will be measured and taken.........
giving everything to Vishnu, Oh! Fool!, now will you live——where! How?
Vamana asks for Boon

paces of ground as covered by my own feet. The wise man never asks for more than what he needs."

Bali looked at Vamana's small dwarf feet and laughed. He said, "Ask a greater boon. Perhaps an island and a large comfortable house with all needs provided!"

But Vamana only said, "My three paces of land is all I ask. It is all I need." Again Bali laughed and said, "So be it, then. Measure your three paces of land." He took the water-pot in his hand, poured some water on to his palm and solemnly promised to grant the dwarf his gift.

At this moment, Sukracharya, the teacher realised that something was afoot. He warned Bali and said, "There is some mischief here. For I am certain that this dwarf is none other than Sri Vishnu Himself. He will cover the three worlds with just two steps of His and then how will you give Him the third? Retract from your promise for it is still not too late. The Vedas allow it when there is grave danger to one's life."

But Bali said, "A word once given I cannot take back. I do not fear either hell or death for myself. But a promise given to a holy Brahmin I must keep, be He, Lord Vishnu, Whom I worship daily, or be he, my worst enemy."

Sukracharya was angry because his word of advice had been disregarded. He cursed Bali and said, "You will lose all your wealth and splendour because you have brushed aside the words of your Guru."

Yet Bali was calm and unmoved. He worshipped the feet of the Brahmin boy. He read out the formal *mantra* of gifting the three paces of land to Vamana. Then his queen, a good and virtuous lady called Vindhyavali, brought a golden pitcher of water. Bali poured out the water and washed Vamana's tiny feet with it. Then he looked up and saw – amazed – that the form of Vamana was wonderously increasing in size. As he looked, Vamana grew bigger and bigger. With his first step he covered the entire earth. With his second, he covered the heavens and the rest of the universe. His body filled the sky and his arms embraced the four directions. Bali and his priests were stunned to see the entire creation in him.

The asuras were mortified at Vamana's apparent treachery. They picked up all their terrible weapons of destruction and attacked Vamana. But the attendants of Sri Vishnu soon put them to flight.

Then Vamana looked at Bali and laughed gently. "You will go to hell if you do not fulfil your promise, king. Where then shall I place My foot for the third pace?"

Bali bowed his head and said, "Lord, if it be Thy pleasure, place Thy foot on my head for Thy third pace. I am forever Thine and Thine alone. That Thou hast taken everything away from me is indeed a blessing for I had become blinded by pride and

. . . .

पदं तृतीयं कुरु शीर्ष्णि मे निजम्　　　　　　(स्क. 8 अ. 22 श्लो. 2)

Thy third-step, Oh, Lord, place upon my head!

Trivikrama form of Vamana

power. Blessed I am, for by the nature of Thy own request, I have lost my kingdom, but I have gained Thee instead."

With all the majesty of his divine glory, Vamana placed his foot on the head of Bali for his third pace of ground! In a soft, loving voice he said, "Son, I take away all from him whom I love. It is a common thing that riches make a man disregard Me. When a man has attained human birth and in him you see the absence of pride of birth, *karma*, youth, beauty, wisdom, power and wealth, then you shall know him to be in My favour."

Bali became one of the seven immortals of the world, for his head was purified by the touch of the Lord's feet!

MATSYA AVATARA

This is the story of how the Lord once incarnated as a fish. We should not find this strange, because the Lord, as we have seen, assumes any form He pleases to serve the purpose He has in hand. This incarnation became necessary because once Brahma happened to lose the Vedas, which were stolen by an asura called Hayagriva, who resided at the bottom of the ocean. And since only a fish can survive best in water. Shri Vishnu took the form of a fish in order to get back the Vedas.

In the South, there once lived a king called Satyavrata. He was a great devotee of Sri Vishnu and performed penance by living only on water. One day he was doing his daily ablutions when a tiny fish came out of his *kamandalu* on to the palm of his hand. The king was large-hearted and generous. He took the poor little fish and put it in the river.

But to his great surprise the fish cried out piteously, "O please do not leave me in this great big river where other creatures are bound to swallow me up!"

So Satyavrata put the fish back into his *kamandalu*, which was full of water. Next morning he saw that the fish had grown in size, had occupied the entire vessel, and was crying out for more space. So he put it in a bigger vessel. And as the size of the fish kept increasing, he kept putting it in bigger and bigger vessels. Till at last it grew so big that he had to put it in a lake.

But the fish filled the lake too with its ever-increasing size. So Satyavrata took the fish and put it in the ocean for he thought that that would be the only place big enough for it. Here too, the fish was not happy, for it was scared that alligators and other animals of the water would kill it!

Now this was really too much for the king, and he was completely perplexed. And then it suddenly occurred to him that this must indeed be Sri Narayana, incarnated for a specific purpose. He folded his hands and said, "I have never before known a fish to grow the way You have grown. I am convinced that You are none other than Sri Narayana, for I know that when the need for it arises, You come down to earth for the

एकदा कृतमालायां कुर्वतो जलतर्पणम् ।
तस्याञ्जलयुदके काचिच्छफर्येकाभ्यपद्यत ॥   (स्क. 8 अ. 24 श्लो. 2)

Satyavrata in the Kritamala river, while doing his water-offerings, in his uplifted palm-of-water came a fish..............

Satyavrata and the fish

welfare of the world. But I am ignorant as to why You have taken the form of a fish. Pray enlighten me, Lord, for I am Your devotee."

And the Lord answered, "On the seventh day from today, the Triloki will be plunged in the waters of *pralaya**. A large boat will then come to you. In the mean-time, go and collect all the herbs, plants, seeds and trees and all the different species of animals. Taking these and the seven Rishis with you, enter the boat. When the storms rock the boat, tie it up with Vasuki, the serpent, to my horn. Do not be afraid. Although it will be dark all around, the light from the Rishis will illumine you. I will support the boat for the duration of the *pralaya*, and you shall gain supreme wisdom from Me."

Satyavrata did as he was told. Sure enough, on the seventh day, the deluge started. There were terrific storms and the clouds rained sheets and sheets of water. The earth's boundaries were lost. There was no heaven, no earth. It was just water and water, masses and masses of it. The good king and the seven sages sat in the boat in deep meditation. Satyavrata prayed to the Lord, "As the impure gold loses all its impurities when it comes in contact with fire, so too the *jiva* sheds all its ignorance when it worships You, O Lord! Please enlighten me with Your knowledge and cut the knots of ignorance in my heart."

And Satyavrata listened, enraptured, as the divine Lord taught him the true nature of the Self. At the end of the *pralaya*, the Lord killed the demon Hayagriva and returned the Vedas to Brahma.

RISHI CHYAVANA

Sharyati was a most learned and pious king. He had a daughter, a lotus-eyed beauty called Sukanya. Once, the king and his daughter with their attendants went into the forest for an outing. There they came across the ashrama of the Rishi Chyavana.

The ashramas of all the Rishis of the past had a wonderfully peaceful atmosphere about them. So the king's friends and attendants wandered about at will, sometimes sitting under the shade of a tree, sometimes plucking its fruit and eating it and some-times refreshing themselves at the cool stream that ran close by.

Sukanya, with her friends, flitted like a fairy among the flowers and bushes of the forest garden. They sang and danced and played games. As they were engaged in fun and sport, Sukanya spotted two streaks of light as those from a glow-worm emerging from within an ant-hill. In her childishness she picked up a thorn and pierced them with it. But she was alarmed beyond measure when blood oozed out of them. At the same time, Sharyati's men discovered that their secretions had stopped and that they could no longer perform their natural functions any more. The king immediately guessed that some harm had been done to the Rishi. Shamefacedly his daughter came up and told him what she had done. The king was greatly agitated. He went in search

---

* deluge

तान्निरीक्ष्य वरारोहा सरूपान् सूर्यवर्चसः ।
अजानती पतिं साध्वी अश्विनौ शरणं ययौ ॥

(स्क. 9 अ. 3 श्लो. 16)

Seeing all the three equally beautiful young and brilliant as the sun, the noble lady not knowing who is her husband, surrenders herself with devotion to the Aswini-pair....... when she got her husband.

Sukanya Appeals

of the Rishi and found him under the mound of earth. He touched the feet of Chyavana and begged his pardon for his daughter's childish conduct. As a compensation for this he offered to give him Sukanya in marriage. The sage forgave him and accepted the girl as his wife.

Now Sukanya was terribly sorry for what she had done. It had taught her a lesson: never again to be so extremely playful. To make up for the wrong she had done, she served the sage faithfully. She studied all his whims and fancies and never offended him if she could help it. Her husband was pleased with her wifely virtues.

One day, the Aswini Kumaras called at Chyavana's hermitage. They were the celestial physicians, who knew the secret of eternal youth. Now Chyavana was old, bent and wrinkled. He had long white hair and he coughed and wheezed with age. To the Aswini twins he said, "O divine physicians! You know the secret of youth. Please give me back my youth and strength. In return I shall secure for you a cup of the *soma* juice at the sacrificial offerings." The Aswini Kumaras agreed, because so far they had been denied a share of the *soma* offerings.

They took the old wrinkled sage to a tank which had been prepared by the Siddhas. Then all three of them plunged into it. When they came out it was as three handsome youths of the most extraordinary vigour and beauty. They were wearing fresh lotus garlands, ear-rings of gold and fine silk dresses. And they all looked alike. When she saw them, the poor princess Sukanya was thoroughly confused. She was shy and abashed and knew not what to do. She could not call out to her husband because it is a custom that an Indian wife does not call her husband by his name. She appealed to the Aswini Kumaras to declare themselves to her, so that she might know the third youth to be her husband. The Aswini Kumaras were pleased with her purity and chastity. They pointed out the Rishi to her and then sped back to the heavens in their aerial chariot.

Chyavana was now very pleased that he had youth and vitality to match his wife's beauty. One day the princess was sitting with her husband when her father, King Sharyati, called at the ashrama. He was surprised, nay, shocked to see his daughter sitting with a youth, handsome and resplendent. Sukanya got up to receive her father and bent down to touch his feet. The king, however rebuked her, saying, "What have you done, you unchaste girl? How could you have the heart to leave your saintly husband because he is old, and to take a lover because of his youth and good looks? Surely you have lost all reason and sense of shame. To think that a daughter of mine could stoop so low! You have indeed brought shame and disgrace to the whole family."

The innocent princess then explained to her father what had happened and told him the story of how the sage had got back his youth. Sharyati then embraced her in joy and gave the couple his blessings. At the request of Sukanya , he performed a *soma* sacrifice in which Chyavana offered some of the *soma* juice to the Aswini Kumaras. Indra was so angered by this, that he picked up his Vajra* to hurl it down at the Rishi.

---

* divine thunderbolt

तदभिद्रवदुद्वीक्ष्य स्वप्रयासं च निष्फलम् ।
दुर्वासा दुद्रुवे भीतो दिक्षु प्राणपरीप्सया ।　　　(स्क. ९ अ. ४ श्लो. ४९)

Durvasa tried his best to stop the Chakra, all in vain. To save himself he started running all round the universe.

The Chakra follows Durvasa

But Chyavana had gained much ascetic power and merit through his rigorous penance, and he paralysed the hands of Indra. The devas pleaded with him to restore the hands of their king. They promised that henceforth, the Aswini Kumaras would get their share of the *soma* juice in all sacrifices, for all times to come.

And so it came about that both the Aswini Kumaras and the Rishi Chyavana were able to fulfil their parts in the agreement.

KING AMBARISHA

Ambarisha was a king, kind and noble. Although he was the ruler of the whole earth and had all the wealth and enjoyments to make a man contented, he cared not for them. For he knew that earthly enjoyments are never lasting and that only the ignorant take delight in them. He was a great *bhakta* of Sri Narayana.

If ever the Lord had a devotee, it was he. At all times his mind was fixed on the lotus feet of Sri Vishnu. He spoke of nothing but the glories of Vaikuntha. He used his hands to clean Sri Narayana's temple; his ears heard only the praises of Sri Narayana. Everywhere his eyes saw expressions of His divinity; everything he touched reminded him of His divine Presence. His nose smelt only the holy fragrance of *Tulasi* which proceeds from the feet of Sri Vishnu. His tongue tasted only the food that had been offered to Lord Narayana. His feet walked the places dear to Him and his head was ever bowed at His lotus feet. He enjoyed doing things in the service of Sri Narayana and if he was attached, it was only to those devoted to Him. He offered to Him the fruits of all his actions and thus, by constantly dedicating himself to Him, he gradually came to give up all his desires. Sri Vishnu was very pleased with him and gave him His *chakra* for his protection.

Once, King Ambarisha and his wife undertook a special fast called the *Dvadasi Vrata*. He practised special disciplines for a whole year. Towards the end, he fasted for three days, and on the fourth day, the twelfth day of the moon, he was to break the fast. On this occasion, he bathed in the waters of the Yamuna and worshipped Sri Narayana at Mathura. He made gifts of his wealth and cattle to the poor and the needy, and distributed his riches among the Brahmins. Next he fed them all and then asked permission to eat himself. At that very moment Rishi Durvasa came there. The king invited him to be his guest. The sage accepted the invitation and then went to the river to bathe and to perform his daily rites.

When he had finished bathing, the Rishi sat down for meditation and soon became absorbed in it. Thus the time slipped by. Ambarisha grew anxious. For if the auspicious hour to break his fast passed away, his *vrata* would be of no avail. Yet if he ate, it would be an insult to an invited guest, and the most wrathful Rishi at that*. So he decided to compromise by sipping a little water which the *Shastras* say is both eating and non-eating. This way he broke his fast without meaning any offence to the sage.

---

* Durvasa was known to have a quick temper.

When Durvasa came back and learnt that the king had taken water, he was very angry, for he thought that Ambarisha had done this purposely in his pride as a monarch. He cursed the king and tore up a tuft of hair which turned into a demon. He then commanded the demon to devour him. But Ambarisha remained calm and was not at all afraid. The *chakra* of Sri Vishnu, however, sprang up for the protection of the king. It moved menacingly towards Durvasa, from whom the curse had come. The demon lost all his power and because Ambarisha stood absolutely unmoved.

Durvasa ran in all directions in a desperate attempt to save himself. But the weapon followed him steadily. At last he ran to Brahma and implored him to save him. Brahma said to him, "Son, you have offended a Vishnu-*bhakta*. I can honestly do nothing to save you."

Then Durvasa went to Shiva and asked for his help. Shiva looked at him compassionately and replied, "I am powerless to do anything. This weapon is too much for me. You will have to ask Sri Vishnu Himself to help you."

The *chakra* was now getting closer and closer to him. In a last bid to escape from the deadly weapon, he appealed to Sri Vishnu for help. Vishnu smiled at him ruefully and said, "Son, I am the slave of My devotees. My heart is in their possession. They cannot live without Me and verily I cannot live without them They are My life as much as I am theirs. My devotees forsake their wives, wealth, children and homes for My sake. How can I forsake them in their hour of need? They have given their hearts to Me. They give up all desires, even that of liberation – all for My sake. With their minds calm, they offer all their service unto Me. Therefore, My child, even I am powerless against the weapon which has been released by My devotee. There is but one way for you out of this. Go to him whom you have offended. Beg his pardon. He is sure to forgive you for your offence."

Durvasa hurried back to where Ambarisha was and fell at his feet. Ambarisha asked the *chakra* to desist from its round of destruction. He showed the Rishi due respect and requested him to come and have his meal. Then Durvasa and Ambarisha had their meal which had been waiting for so long.

Soon after, Ambarisha made over his kingdom to his eldest son and retired to the forest, there to plunge his mind into meditation upon the Lord.

THE STORY OF KING RANTIDEVA

Those were the glorious days in ancient India when men were honest and truthful and kings were ever engaged in striving for the welfare of their people. In such times there once lived a king whose name was Rantideva. He had a large and generous heart and every being came within his embrace of love for he saw Lord Hari in every living creature.

Rantideva was always making gifts to the poor and the needy. He said to himself, "The Lord gives me all these things in plenty. Should I then sit back and enjoy them when so many mouths of Sri Hari are yet to be fed? I shall not be in want, because He has made me His instrument to scatter His blessings in the world."

And sure enough, he would always have plenty of food and clothing to distribute. The king was famous in the world for his warm hospitality which he extended to rich and poor alike. Whenever anyone was in trouble, he would go to the king. And whenever Rantideva was of service to anyone, he would feel that it was a service unto Sri Hari. Thus he gave a mother's love to his people. Like a child runs to its mother with its troubles, hurts and pains, so too his subjects would go to him. He would try to remove the cause of their sorrow and if he was unable to do so, it would pain him immensely.

Thus passed many years of prosperity and people basked in the generous love of their king.

But then a time came when the country was hit by famine. The crops failed, the cattle died and men, women and children starved in large numbers. They flocked to the gates of the king's palace. Rantideva would sit and pray, "O Lord, give me the strength to remove their suffering." Then he would go out and distribute to his people what little he had left. And yet the famine continued. In fact it grew worse from day to day. And there was a time when he did not have enough to eat for himself. He could not even feed his family. For none of the members of his household ate unless the masses had been fed. Sometimes there would be food for them, but the king would have to go hungry. Nevertheless, he was happy, because his mind was satisfied when his people were fed. As the conditions grew worse, he did not have anything left to give to the hungry and the starving. No help came to him. And yet his faith in Sri Hari only increased. Day after day, the king and his dependents starved and the famine persisted.

When the king had thus fasted for forty-eight days, someone brought him a bowl of porridge made of flour, milk and ghee. By this time the king was in no position to even move, so weak had he become due to continuous starvation. Overcome by hunger and thirst, Rantideva and his family were indeed glad to see an unexpected meal before them. They were about to eat when there came to the door, a wrinkled old Brahmin, much in need of food. The king received him respectfully and gave him some of the porridge to eat. As they were about to eat again, a beggar came to the door. His face appeared pinched with hunger, so Rantideva gave him too, some of the meal to eat. Then there came a sweeper and he brought with him his dogs. He looked at the king pitifully and said, "Maharaj! My dogs and I have not had any food for many days now. We are starving for want of food. Now we have come to you , for if you will not help us, who will?" So the king gave him the remaining porridge.

Now the king and his family had again no food to eat. There was just a little drink left. Just then, came a Chandala, his throat parched with thirst, his eyes heavy with exhaustion. He begged the king to moisten his dry lips with a little bit of water. Rantideva saw him as yet another form of Sri Hari and held the cup to his cracked lips. He prayed to the Lord and said, "Please, Lord! I do not care for the rewards of this earth. Nor do

इति प्रभाष्य पानीयं म्रियमाण: पिपासया ।
पुल्कसायाददाद्धीरो निसर्गकरुणो नृप: ॥   (स्क. 9 अ. 21 श्लो. 14)

Thinking thus the heroic king, who was dying to drink because of his great thirst, gave the "drink" to the scavenger . . . . the King was born with kindness towards others.

Rantideva Gives away his last morsel

I care for powers of any kind. My only prayer is – give me the capacity to feel the pain of others and the power to serve them. Let me not ever be indifferent to their sorrows and their sufferings. Make me Thy instrument to give them relief, to make them happy."

The man drank the water. The sparkle of life came back into his eyes. And wonderfully enough, the king felt his own hunger, thirst and fatigue dropping away from him. He felt refreshed and fulfilled, as a hungry man is after a good and satisfying meal. Suddenly there appeared before him Maya and all her attendants. She smiled at him and said, "O King, I am indeed pleased to see your devotion and your extraordinary love for your people. You have suffered much. If you worship me now, I can remove all your wants for all time to come. I can give you the riches and the entire wealth of the world."

Rantideva showed them due respect, but only as the different forms of Hari. He asked Maya for nothing, for his mind was absorbed in Sri Hari. He said to her, "I have no use for all the riches you have to offer me. I have no wish to live any longer than I have to. I do not hanker for the enjoyments of the world, because my mind does not run after them."

And Maya, the queen of the world, the mistress of all beings, the consort of Sri Vishnu, fled from his presence with her whole retinue of attendants. She vanished like a dream does when a person awakes.

Then Rantideva was blessed by the presence of the Lord Himself. He worshipped Him and prayed that he might never be separated from Him. In time, Rantideva became one of the greatest yogis of the land. He merged himself in meditation. By his wonderful service to his people and his love for all living creatures whom he worshipped as Sri Hari, he attained the blissful Being of Lord Narayana.

———————

PART II

ॐ श्रीपरमात्मने नमः

Kamsa

Once again Mother Earth was in trouble. She suffered under the weight of inhumanities practised by the daityas. She could bear the burden no more. So she took the form of a cow, and with tears rolling down her cheeks, she went to Brahma, the father, and implored him to do something about it. Brahma took pity on her and taking Shiva and the devas with him, he went to Sri Vishnu's abode. There he worshipped the Preserver of the Universe and then entered into deep meditation. And within his heart he heard a voice saying that the Lord already knew the troubles of the earth, that He would incarnate in the house of Vasudeva and that the celestials would also take birth to aid Him in His mission.

*   *   *

Devaki was the princess of Mathura. Ugrasena, the king, was her father, and the powerful and wicked Kamsa was her brother. She was a cultured young lady, both virtuous and beautiful. She was given in marriage to a noble young man called Vasudeva. After the marriage ceremony, Vasudeva took his bride away in their chariot which was loaded with gifts, beautiful and costly, which they had received. Now Kamsa was very fond of his sister. So he declared that he himself would drive the chariot to Vasudeva's house. The procession started to the sound of conches, drums and trumpets. Everyone was feeling happy and was in a mood of joy and merriment. Devaki herself glowed with the happiness of a bride. And even though she was a little sad at leaving her home, her eyes sparkled with the adventure of the new life beginning for her. And she was proud that the chariot was to be driven by no less a person than Kamsa himself!

As the procession moved, the chariot rolled merrily along. Everyone was laughing and singing and joking. Kamsa took the reins of the horses in his own hands. The proud monarch made a striking picture as he urged the horses forward. But all the fun and merriment stopped suddenly when a heavenly voice cut across like the crack of a whip. It said, "Fool! Know that the eighth child born of this very girl you are driving now shall be the cause of your death!" Kamsa's face changed suddenly. It became ugly and distorted. His eyes became bloodshot. He lunged at Devaki and caught her by the hair. Swiftly, he drew forth his sword and was about to cut her head off, when Vasudeva restrained his hand and in a gentle, pacifying tone said, "Kamsa, you are a noble king. Why do you want to suffer the disgrace of killing a woman, your own sister at that, on the very day of her marriage? Look at her, how terrified she is. We all have to die, whether now or after a hundred years. Devaki is innocent and helpless. Besides, not she, but the eighth child of her womb shall be the cause of your death. So desist from this terrible action."

But Kamsa was hard and adamant. He was not at all moved by Vasudeva's pleas. Vasudeva thought quickly and said, "If you spare Devaki's life now, I promise to hand over to you all her offspring when they are born." Now this arrangement found favour with Kamsa. He put his sword away and ordered the wedding procession to move on. Vasudeva felt relieved that he was able to ward off the present danger. He prayed to the Lord and hoped that the future would take care of itself. Lord's Grace divine is always with His sincere and true devotees.

In due course, the first child, a bonny boy, was born to Vasudeva and Devaki. True to his word, Vasudeva took the babe to Kamsa and handed it over to him. Kamsa appreciated this gesture of honesty and gave the child back, saying that he had nothing to fear from it since it would be the eighth child of Devaki who would cause his death.

Now as Kamsa was sitting, feeling happy with his generous gesture, Narada came to him. His eyes twinkled mischievously as he said, "What have you done, Maharaj? Do you not know that all of Devaki's children are to be rays of Lord Vishnu? Narayana will incarnate as her eighth child. All His supporters in Vaikuntha have already taken birth in the Yadava clan. They will also help Him to fight you and the other daityas. Be careful, Kamsa. Do not take any risk. Narayana! Narayana!!" And as quietly as he had come, he left. His work was done, and the name of the Lord was upon his lips.

Sweat broke out over Kamsa's brow. His mind was in great consternation. Although he already knew his fate, this was still an alarming and shocking bit of news, particularly because it came from the special messenger of Narayana. He issued orders to put Vasudeva and Devaki in jail. They were bound with fetters and chains and thrown into the darkest dungeons. He took no risk with Devaki's children. As each one of them was born, he had it seized and put to death instantly. In this manner he did away with seven of his nephews.

And then Devaki was once again big with child. She shone with divine lustre and looked the very picture of auspiciousness. Even Kamsa did not fail to notice that his sister had a special glow about her. Now he was certain that she carried his fated enemy in her womb. He had an irresistible desire to kill her there and then. It would be an easy way to do away with his foe. But then he thought of the sin and shame he would incur for having killed a helpless, pregnant woman. No, he would wait till his hated enemy was born, and then he would show them all that nobody could kill Kamsa. Why, what did he have to fear? He would take the baby as soon as it was born and that would be the end of it. It was as simple as that. And although he had worked this out so carefully in his wicked mind, he knew no peace. For something gnawed at his heart. He would sit day and night consumed by worry and anxiety. He put his father into jail and seized the throne himself. He grew hard and cruel and people became afraid of his power and tyranny. His score of wicked deeds piled high. And yet with all the power and strength in the world, his nerves were completely shattered. The most feared king of the world sat, nervously biting his nails, awaiting the birth of his enemy.

सत्यव्रतं सत्यपरं त्रिसत्यं
सत्यस्य योनिं निहितं च सत्ये ।
सत्यस्य सत्यमृतसत्यनेत्रं
सत्यात्मक त्वां शरणं प्रपन्नाः ॥

We surrender to Thee,
Oh! Lord of Truth,
Who art true
In Thy good wishes,
to Whom
Truth is the highest,
Who is
the same
in all the three
periods of time………
the same
in all the three
States of Consciousness………
Who is
the very source
for Maya,
ever established
in Truth,
the Truth Supreme
in the Creator himself,
Who is one
Who guides all Vedic
thoughts and actions,
and Who is
of the nature
of Truth, Himself.

It was midnight. Kamsa's palace was enveloped in darkness. Men of goodness and purity were at their prayer and worship. The constellation Rohini was rising in the heavens. The stars shone with an unearthly beauty. In the heavens the devas played divine music. The gandharvas and the apsaras sang and danced. On earth, the flames of the sacrificial fires which had been suppressed by Kamsa suddenly shot up. The celestials waited with bated breath, for, on earth was to take place the most blessed event in all times to come.

The helpless and friendless Vasudeva and Devaki sat cold and desolate in the prison. Fervently they prayed to the Lord and asked Him to protect them and their child. The hour was at its darkest. Devaki swooned. And suddenly the room was filled with a brilliant light. It seemed as if a second sun had arisen. Their eyes dazzled, Vasudeva and Devaki could barely look at the source of the light. For there stood Lord Vishnu Himself, in all His divine magnificence! In His four hands He held the Conch (*Shankha*), the Discus (*Chakra*), the Club (*Gada*), and the Lotus-flower (*Padma*). His bosom bore the mark of *Srivatsa*, and on his chest shone the *Kaustubha* gem. He was dressed in golden yellow silk and the diadem of His brow sparkled with the glitter of its magnificent, unearthly, precious gems.

Vasudeva and Devaki bowed before Him, and in that moment all the grief and suffering of the by-gone years vanished. Their eyes were lit with the light of love as they gazed upon the enchanting dark-complexion of the Lord. Sri Vishnu blessed the couple and then spoke to them. "Father, mother," he said, "your days of sorrow are now over. Too long has the earth borne the burden of the wicked deeds of the impious. I have manifested Myself for their destruction. Father, take Me now to the house of your good friend Nanda, in Gokula. His wife, Yasoda, has just given birth to a baby girl. Exchange Me for that daughter and place Me by Yasoda's side. Bring the little girl here into the prison. Nothing shall bar your way. You and mother Devaki will both attain My being by meditating upon Me as your Son as well as the Supreme Brahman".

And then the light was no more. By Devaki's side lay a little dark baby, whose complexion was like that of a rain-bearing cloud. The mother lifted him into her arms and kissed his sweet face. She fondled and rocked him. Then silently, Vasudeva took the baby from her. Devaki thought her heart would break. But then she remembered the words of the Lord, and derived her comfort from them. She composed herself and fixed her mind on Adi Narayana. As Vasudeva moved towards the door, the strangest thing happened. The chains that bound him dropped away of their own accord. One after another, the doors of the prison swung open. The guards had fallen into an unnatural deep slumber. And within moments, he found himself walking through the streets of Mathura.

It had now started raining. There was nobody on the streets. People were fast asleep in their own homes. Carrying the divine baby, Vasudeva arrived at the banks of the river Yamuna. The waters were twirling and swirling in an angry flood. Suddenly, the waters parted and a ford appeared between them. Vasudeva walked through the river, carrying the baby high above his head, lest the waters should touch it. The celestial

देवकी –

उपसंहर विश्वात्मन्नदो रूपमलौकिकम्

शंखचक्रगदापद्याश्रिया जुष्टं चतुर्भुजम् ॥ (स्क. 10 अ. 2 श्लो. 26)

Devaki cried—Oh Lord fold up this Thy unearthly form, with four-arms, bearing the Conch, the Discus, the Mace and the Lotus.

Lord Vishnu Blesses Devaki, Vasudeva in Prison

thousand-hooded Seshanaga protected and guarded them as a moving unbrella for the divine load of Beauty

When Vasudeva arrived at Gokula, he saw that everything was absolutely hushed and quiet. He entered the house of Nanda. Yasoda, his wife, was fast asleep. By her side lay a baby girl. Quietly, Vasudeva picked her up, and in her place he put the little baby-boy. Then he crept away and came back to Mathura. He gave the baby-girl to Devaki. Then slowly, the prison gates, by themselves, closed on him, and he found himself in chains again.

When the guards heard the lusty yell of a baby coming from the prison chamber, they hastened to give Kamsa the news. The sky was still dark and the hour was just before dawn. Kamsa was having nightmares and bad dreams. He woke up with a start. He was still in the stupor of dazed sleep, rudely awakened. With dishevelled hair and bleary eyes he stumbled towards the dungeon. Devaki saw the leery expression in his eyes and clutched the baby closer, and retreated into a corner of the prison.

"No, no! Not this one too!" she cried piteously. "Leave me this little baby. You have snatched all my innocent children so far. Besides, this one is only a girl. What harm can she do to you?" But she saw that Kamsa was unrelenting and she hugged the baby in one last motherly embrace. The wicked king snatched the child from her hands and lifting it high in the air, was about to dash it against the stone wall, when, lo! the infant slipped from his fingers and rose up into the air. Suddenly, she became the shining resplendent goddess Lakshmi. "Fool!", she cried. "You will gain nothing from destroying innocent children. Your enemy has already been born and when the time comes, he shall indeed destroy you. Dare you hope to avert the will of the Lord?"

Kamsa was wonder-struck. He trembled violently and then came to his senses. He removed the fetters and the chains of Vasudeva and Devaki and fell at their feet. "Forgive me for my wicked deeds," he said. "Like a rakshasa, a hard-hearted stone, I have killed your innocent babies. The Lord will indeed have a terrible punishment in store for me for these, my heinous sins." Vasudeva and Devaki felt sorry for him and forgave him readily.

Kamsa then called the daitya counsellors together and told them what had happened. Now they all had stupid asuric minds, so their thinking was clouded. They gave him serious counsel and advised him to kill all the infants born within the last ten days in the entire kingdom. They said, "Kill them all, O brave king. Do away with the enemy of the asuras. At the most the devas will attack us. And we all know how they fear your arrows. Give us the orders. Permit us to destroy Vishnu. He is the strengh behind the devas. Once this Omnipotent Power-divine is removed, how can the gods survive? Brahmins, cows, Vedas, asceticism, control of the mind and the senses, faith, kindness, tolerance and sacrifice are the limbs of Vishnu. We shall destroy all these too. We believe in a purely materialistic, secular life. Where we succeed, how can Vishnu survive?"

Kamsa, because he himself had a basically wicked mind, was easily caught in the maze of their asuric arguments. The prospect of doing away with his enemy appealed

ववर्ष पर्जन्य उपांशुगर्जितः
शेषोऽन्वगाद्वारि निवारयन् फणैः ।

(स्क.10 अ. 3 श्लो.50)

मघोनि वर्षत्यसकृद्यमानुजा
गंभीर तोयौघ जवोर्मिफेनिला ।
भयानकावर्तशताकुला नदी
मार्गं ददौ सिन्धुरिव प्रियः पते ॥   (श्लो. 51)

The rain was heavy. "Sesha", spread its hood as an umbrella and followed the Lord's first procession. Indra rained heavily. The Yamuna, sister of Yama, was swollen in floods, terrible in her force of flow, her whirls and froth and bubbles — and she gave a path for Vasudeva to carry the Baby Divine across— as the ocean gave way for Sri Ramachandraji! ·

Baby Krishna being carried to Gokulam

to him very much. He directed the daityas to oppress all good people and to put all their own suggestions into practice.

GOKULA

In Gokula there was great joy. Mother Yasoda woke up in the morning to find a beautiful little baby lying by her side. She looked at him and was overwhelmed with happiness. Here was the little one, all her very own. Here was a joy beyond words, for the world had never seen such a lovely child before! Hers was the joy of total fulfilment.

Soon, the entire household, nay, the entire village came to know that in Nanda's house was born a most heavenly child. Nanda was the chief of the Yadava clan. The rejoicings were on a large scale. The streets were swept clean. Flower garlands were hung at the door of every house. Clean fresh water was sprinkled on the roads, and all along, they were decorated with flags, buntings and flower-arches. In Nanda's house, the Brahmins chanted Vedic hymns and invoked upon the child the blessings of the Lord. Nanda gave cattle and wealth in plenty to the Brahmins and to the poor. The *Sutas* sat and recited from the *puranas*. Minstrels sang of the valiant deeds of the heroes of old and of the ancient kings. The musicians played on their instruments. The *gopas* (cowherds) wore fresh clothes and smeared their foreheads with sandal-paste and wound their way to Nanda's house to wish him well. The *gopis* wore their best garments which were of the most brightly coloured hues and shades. They lined their eyes with collyrium and wore jasmine in their hair. Then with their swirling skirts swishing from side to side they laughed and danced their way to Nanda's house. In scented-water they mixed oil and turmeric and sprinkled it on each other for good luck.

The *gopis* perhaps had the greatest fun of them all. They took for Yasoda presents of curd, butter and milk. They took turns with each other to fondle and caress the baby. Some praised his dark complexion, some his black curls, some his twinkling eyes and some his smile of pure joy. This was an important occasion for the simple men and women of the Yadava-clan and they bubbled over with happiness. They sang and danced to the rhythm of tambourines and cymbals, flutes and lyres. They gave thanks to the Lord and chanted divine hymns in His praise and glory. And what had started for them in irrepressible merriment ended in rapturous ecstasy.

POOTHANA AND TRINAVARTA

Now Kamsa came to know that a baby boy had been born in the house of Nanda at Gokula. Nothing could be proved, but nevertheless he had a sneaking suspicion that it must be his dreaded enemy. So all his efforts were aimed at getting rid of that child. His crooked mind worked out all kinds of schemes to put the infant to death.

Poothana was the most frightful and dreaded of rakshasis. She was treacherous and villainous to the very core of her being. She knew all kinds of magical tricks and spells which helped her in the asuric work she did for Kamsa. She was an Indian witch.

निशाचरीत्थं व्यथितस्तना व्यसु —
व्यार्दाय केशांश्चरणौ भुजावपि ।
प्रसार्य गोष्ठे निजरूपमास्थिता
वज्राहतो वत्र इवापतन्नृप ।

(स्क. 10 अ. 6 श्लो. 13)

With a bleeding breast Poothana fell back in the cow-shed stretching her limbs, her hair flying out, assuming her real ugly form——and the Lord innocently played upon her dead bosom!

Baby Krishna kills Poothana

At Kamsa's behest, she entered Gokula. By her secret powers she transformed herself into a lovely lady. She wore garments of shimmering silk and decked herself with the most gorgeous ornaments. The fragrance of the jasmine in her hair had the strangest power of attraction. With a graceful sway of her hips, casting sidelong glances, she made her way to Nanda's house. Nobody even thought of barring her way, for she was extremely well-dressed and looked as though she came from a very high family. She went up to where mother Yasoda was sitting with her little baby. She cooed over the child in a honeyed voice. Yasoda was really impressed by this magnificent stranger.

Poothana then begged to hold the infant in her arms for a few moments. Very sweetly she asked Yasoda if she could plant a little kiss on the child's forehead. How could the proud mother refuse such a simple request? Then the wicked demoness suckled the child to her breast which was full of the deadliest poison. By this time she had already gone out of the courtyard of the house under the pretence of entertaining the baby. What she in her stupidity did not know, was that he was none other than the Lord Himself. He clutched at her breast with both his tiny hands and sucked hard. He sucked and sucked till he had drawn out not only all the poison but also the very life-breath of the rakshasi!

At once she regained her old hideous form and screamed out aloud, "Enough, enough! Let go! No more, no more!!" She gasped and writhed and struggled, all in vain. For, the child would not leave her till he had sucked the last drop of life from her. She twisted her body this way and that, kicked her hands and legs helplessly about with all the strength she could muster, and she perspired profusely. Her hair got mangled with the dust and her entire body shook so violently that it set the earth trembling. Finally, she crashed to the ground with a roar that resounded in the three worlds. People scattered in fear and all the trees within twelve miles radius fell down uprooted.

Then all was quiet.

Mother Yasoda came hurrying out to see what had happened to her baby. Oh, what a relief it was to see that her darling was absolutely unharmed. But to her horror she saw that he was playing happily on the dead carcass of an awful demoness! She held him close and kissed his little brow over and over again. She shuddered to think what her fate would have been had the rakshasi succeeded in her plot! But the baby, apparently oblivious to the sensation he had created, smiled contentedly, and snuggling into his mother's arms, promptly fell fast asleep.

The people of Gokula then chopped Poothana's body into pieces and set fire to it over logs of wood. It was evening and the night curtain was slowly falling over the village. The flames from the pyre licked high and the curling smoke went up. A lovely fragrance spread everywhere. Even the *tamasic* body of a hideous sorceress had been purified by the touch of the Lord!

When Kamsa came to know that Poothana had failed in her task, he summoned to him an asura whose name was Trinavarta. This asura was cunning and tricky and his ways were more demoniacal than Poothana's.   He could raise dust-storms and whirlwinds at a moment's notice, and could easily sweep away into a cyclone the heaviest objects on the earth.

One day, Yasoda was sitting with her baby on her lap in her court-yard, when suddenly she felt him grow heavier. Every moment his weight increased, till at last he grew so heavy that she had to put him down. This was a strange thing to happen and she grew frightened lest it forebode evil. She ran into the village to find if anyone could explain to her the meaning of this strange phenomenon. In the meantime, Trinavartasura saw his chance to do his dirty mischief. He raised a terrific storm. The wind raised a blinding dust which clouded the whole atmosphere. Dust got into the hair, eyes and mouths of people.   They could see nothing.   Their breathing got choked.   They stumbled and clutched at any support they could find. Gokula had never known such a tornado before. And with all the force and power he could muster, the rakshasa lifted the baby high up into the swirling wind. Mother Yasoda put out her hands to feel for her little one. But she could not reach him anywhere. She screamed loudly and then swooned away.

Meanwhile, the demon was using all his strength to lift the baby higher and higher. But he found it increasingly difficult to do so, because with every passing moment he grew more and more in weight. He clutched at the throat of the rakshasa and tightened his grasp on it.   Trinavarta started choking. It was his plan to lift the child to a great height and then to dash it to the ground, so that escape from death would be impossible. But his plan was properly foiled.   The child grew heavier and heavier and the asura gasped more and more for breath. At last the agony became too much for Trinavarta.   Like a heavy stone hurtling down, he fell through the air, the whirlwind of his own creation, and crashed upon a rock. His body was shattered to pieces and his eyeballs popped out of their sockets.   Like a huge mountain he lay there; he was senseless and quite dead.

The dust had now settled and the air had cleared. But the baby was lost. Nowhere could he be seen. Till at last, a search party found him on the outskirts of Gokula playing on the lifeless body of the rakshasa. Yasoda was hysterical with tears and laughter at finding her baby safe and sound. She kissed him again and again, and held him as though she would never let him go. When they got home, she gave him his feed, for the poor little fellow was hungry. Then she put her fingers to his tiny mouth to wipe the milk off from his lips. In a sleepy yawn, he opened wide his mouth. And there Yasoda saw the entire universe – sun, moon, stars, mountains, rivers, oceans, animals, birds and everything in the cosmos. Overwhelmed by such an inexplicable vision, she trembled and closed her eyes. But her divine son was to show her many more wonderful things.

THE NAMING CEREMONY

Vasudeva had another son by Rohini whom he had also given in Nanda's care. And the time came when he wanted both boys to be named. So he summoned Garga Rishi, who was the Guru of the Yadavas and asked him to perform the ceremonies.

Garga said, "It would indeed be a pleasure to do this for you. But have you thought of what would happen if Kamsa came to know that your Guru had performed a ceremony of this kind in Nanda's house? Would he not then suspect the child to be yours and not Nanda's? No, it is too dangerous."

But Vasudeva was not to be put off so easily. He said, "That is my responsibility, revered teacher. We shall perform the ceremony very quietly and to be on the safe side, we shall hold it in the *goshala**, where nobody will suspect that anything is going on." Vasudeva was anxious to have this purificatory rite performed as soon as possible because of the recent disasters which had threatened the child and also because Garga was a Rishi of great spiritual power.

And so the day was fixed. The sage performed the ceremony and then named the children. "The elder of the two shall be called Rama because of his charming and virtuous ways, and Bala because of his extraordinary strength. He shall also be called Samkarshana because he will unite the Yadavas together.

"This other boy assumes different colours in different ages. This time he has a dark-complexion, therefore, he shall be called Krishna. Being the son of Vasudeva, he shall also be known as Vaasudeva. He has many names, forms and attributes. No one ever knows them fully. He will give you great joy and blessing. He shall save you from many mishaps as he has saved others in the past. Those who love him wholeheartedly shall never know danger or fear. He has all the qualities of Narayana. Know him to be the same."

Having made these profound statements, Garga blessed the two boys and left Gokula.

Balarama and Krishna were now growing up fast. Slowly, they started crawling on their hands and knees, and before long they were toddling unsteadily from one place to another. They wandered anywhere their chubby little legs would take them. There was not a place in Gokula they had not crawled to. They loved to hear the sound of their own tinkling anklet bells, and this would take them further and further away from home. Then, as if frightened, they would turn towards home as soon as their little legs would take them and rush into the open arms of their waiting mothers.

As the days went by, the boys became more and more naughty, particularly Krishna, who was the more mischievous of the two. He would pull the tails of the calves and allow himself to be dragged all over the place. His mother would be full of anxiety and a time came when she could not give her full attention to the house because she had to keep a constant watch over Krishna. Balarama, of course, gave his little brother a hand in everything he did.

Krishna had a partiality for milk, butter and curds. So all his efforts would be directed in procuring these goodies. In the afternoon when the hot sun made everyone

---

* cow-shed

स्तेयं स्वाद्म-यथा दधि पयः
कल्पितैः स्तेययोगे :   (स्क. 10 अ. 8 श्लो. 29)

Eating hungrily the stolen curd and milk, He practised the planned "Theft-Yoga."

Bala Krishna steals Butter

doze, he would tiptoe stealthily into the kitchen, not only his own, but also that of the neighbours. He would signal to his cronies to come and aid him in his little acts of mischief. Together they would break the mud-pots and salvage delicious fresh butter and creamy curds. Because of their inefficiency in eating, they would invariably get their hands and faces properly smeared with butter and cream. Whatever remained they would give to the monkeys and the calves. Now when the *gopis* found out that the scamps had been at their pots of butter and cream, they would go to Yasoda and sorely complain to her about the pranks of her beloved son. Yasoda would catch him by the ear and drag him out to be punished. But Krishna would look at her with such a pathetic mixture of pure innocence and unconfessed guilt, that she would not have the heart to punish him. He would hang his head in shame and look really sorry for what he had done. But the moment his mother had forgiven him, he would run off and get back to all his old forms of mischief, working out in his little brain devilish schemes to make them more varied and interesting.

One day, Balarama and a few other little boys complained to Yasoda that Krishna had swallowed handfuls of mud. So she scolded him for it. But he only looked at her with his big black eyes and said, "Mother, I? Swallow mud? That's not true. You may examine my mouth, if you think I am lying." "Open it," she said. He opened wide his mouth, and lo! once again she saw in it the whole of creation! Yasoda was dazed. She bowed her head before the Lord and said, "If You are indeed the absolute Brahman, then my salutations to You. For, it is by Your *maya* that I appear as Yasoda, and this Child as my Son." Then slowly, her mind came back, from this supreme revelation to her world in Gokula. She picked up the rascally little Krishna and kissed him tenderly with motherly love, for once again he was her own little boy!

KUBERA'S SONS RELEASED

A festival was on. Everyone was busy preparing for it. People were running here and there, now setting up the festoons, now sprinkling the streets with water, now getting the carnivals ready, and now preparing the spicy foods and delicious sweetmeats. No one had time for anything else.

In Nanda's house, the maidservants were all busy, hustling and bustling to and fro with *thalis* of flowers, *chandan* and *kumkum* for worship. Some were engaged in decorating the house to look festive. Others were bent over the fires in the huge open kitchens where food for the many was being cooked. So Yasoda had to look to the boiling of the milk and the churning of the curds herself.

She put the milk on the fire to boil and sat down a little distance away to churn the curds. As she pulled the rope to turn the churner, swinging to right and left, slowly, gracefully, she sang softly to the rhythmic sound of the movements in the mud-pot. And the songs she sang were of the pranks of naughty Krishna. Nothing gave her greater pleasure than to think about them over and over again, for her mind was always filled with him.

Bala Bhāgavatam

उत्ख्लहं विकर्षन्तं दाम्ना बद्धं च बालकम्
कस्येदं कुत आश्चर्यमुत्पात इति कातरा:

(स्क. 10 अ. 11 श्लो. 3)

The assembled parents and cow-boys.....seeing the one bound to the mortars, and dragging it everywhere.....and the two trees fallen down wondered : " Who did. it? How? What a wonder?" Everyone kept on thus asking, as if they were a crowd of foolish ignorant people.

Kubera's Sons Released

After some time, Krishna, hungry from his deeds of mischief, toddled up to his mother, grubby and tired. He climbed on to her lap and asked to be fed. Yasoda smiled at him indulgently and gave him his feed. But just then, the milk on the fire caught her eye. It was about to boil over. So she put her baby down hastily and hurried over to the fire. Now Krishna was annoyed at this. So he broke the mud-pot containing the curds. Then he ran away to a quiet corner and feasted on the butter. When he had had his fill and messed up his face properly with it, he distributed the remaining butter among the monkeys. This he thoroughly enjoyed. He teased the monkeys with the butter first and then gave it to them generously. Then he danced around and clapped his hands in joy and his dangling ear-rings caught the sparkling rays of the sun.

Yasoda came back to her churning and found her pot broken. She looked around for the culprit but could not find him anywhere. Finally she found him in the court-yard, feeding the monkeys. He looked up at her in startled innocence and then seeing that she was determined to punish him, he started running as fast as his little legs would carry him. But Yasoda chased him with a stick, "Wait till I catch you, you little rascal! The *gopis* are right. From the moment you get up in the morning till the time you are in bed at night, you are nothing but a big nuisance. This time I shall punish you good and proper. I'll teach you a lesson." Krishna panted ahead but Yasoda was not far behind. At last she caught him and would have spanked him too, but she saw big tears running down his cheeks and he rubbed his eyes with his tiny knuckles. Her gentle heart melted. So she decided to tie him up instead.

She took a length of rope and tied him to the mortar. But the rope fell short by two inches. So she ran into the house and got another length of rope. This time it looked long enough but again it fell short by two inches. So she went and got some more rope. And still it was short. Exasperated now, Yasoda went and borrowed a few lengths of rope from the neighbours. But no matter how many pieces she joined together, strange! it always fell short by two inches! She just could not understand this. By now she was perspiring and her hair had become loose and dishevelled. She looked at him in utter despair mingled with shame and embarrassment. Despair because the whole thing made absolutely no sense to her, and shame and embarrassment because, well, he was her own son, was he not? And to think that she could not even tie him up when she wanted to! Krishna knew her thoughts and laughed inwardly at her obvious confusion. Then knowing that she could not take any more teasing, he allowed himself to be bound.

This is the way the Lord plays with those who love Him. It is an endless game of 'catch me if you can'. Nobody can, but ultimately He yields to the will of the sincere devotee and allows Himself to be bound, not by ropes and chains, but by the very nature of their all-consuming, overpowering love for Him!

The musician can never be without his song. The artist is automatically drawn towards his canvas and brushes. The dancer is thrilled by the sound of jingling bells. The mischievous thrive on mischief. So here was Krishna, itching to do something naughty, but tied to a huge mortar, many times his weight and size! As he sat there, just a little glum, his eye caught sight of two *arjuna* trees, standing side by side. So he stood up and waddled up to them with the mortar dragging heavily behind. Now the mortar got wedged between the trees and Krishna gave a hard pull to get himself free. Both trees came crashing down, trunks, roots and all. Two shining beings flew out and the space shone with their light. They bowed before Krishna and sang hymns in his praise. These two heavenly beings, who were the sons of Kubera, the god of wealth, were drunk with pride and were at one time cursed by Narada, to whom they had shown disrespect. Narada had told them that they would remain imprisoned in the *arjuna* trees till a time when Krishna would come and liberate them.

When they heard the crash, Yasoda and some of the *gopis* came running out to see what had happened. Some of the *gopa* boys had watched everything and they related to them the whole incident. But it was hard for the young mothers to believe this. For there was the cherub, wedged between the *arjuna* trees playing in the mud as if nothing out of the ordinary had happened! And yet, there lay the trees prostrate on the ground. What were they to make of this? Why was it always Krishna who got into scrapes? The *gopas* and *gopis* of Vraja loved him very deeply indeed, and this they could not explain. But they had yet to learn of his divine nature and the purpose of the games he played with them.

THE FRUIT SELLER

"Fruits! Come and buy my juicy fruits!" It was noon, and with the sun directly overhead, it was hot too. The cry of the fruit-seller broke upon the stillness of the day. Little Krishna heard the cry and ran out, for he liked juicy fruit. The fruit-seller saw that he had nothing to give her, but she liked his sweet innocent looks and charming smile. She took her basket down and hunted around for the best of her fruits, with which she filled his little hands. Krishna's baby face lit up with delight, and he put into her basket, two handfuls of paddy. And lo! when she picked up her basket again, the paddy had turned into gold and diamonds and other precious gems!

VRINDAVANA

One day all the elders of Gokula got together at Nanda's house. They talked about the recent calamities that had befallen their village. Gokula had always been peaceful. Never had the simple village folk seen such strange phenomena. Never had they been so troubled and disturbed by the constant tricks and plots of the rakshasas. They decided that it was now much too dangerous to stay in Gokula, and that a solution to their problem had to be found.

Upananda was the wisest and the oldest of them all. He looked at them gravely and said, "Of late, Vraja has been visited by many misfortunes. By some stroke of luck the child was saved from the baby-killing rakshasi. Only by the grace of Sri Vishnu did he escape the demon, Trinavartasura. And Sri Vishnu alone saved him from being crushed by the *arjuna* trees. Gokula has now become unsafe for all of us. It would be foolish to stay on.

"Let us therefore migrate to a forest called Vrindavana. It is cool and undisturbed and the grass is always green. It is the best place for our cattle and our people. The *gopas*, *gopis* and the cattle will all enjoy the lovely surroundings of Vrindavana with the holy Yamuna flowing close by. Let us get our carts and carriages ready. Send the cows and their calves in advance. Have I your consent?"

"Yes! Yes! Well said! Well said!" cried the elders with one voice.

So the decision was taken. That very night, the people of Vraja packed up their possessions and belongings. They yoked the oxen to the carriages, and put the women, children and old people on them first. The cows were driven in advance. The people followed, beating drums and blowing conches. The *gopis* dangled their legs over the sides of the carts and merrily sang songs as they went along. All the children were excited and the mothers had to keep an eye on them to keep them out of mischief.

At last they arrived at Vrindavana. Krishna and Balarama were full of joy when they saw the green pasture lands of Vrindavana, the sacred hill Govardhana in the distance, and the rippling waters of the Yamuna.

When the boys had grown a little older, they were given the calves to graze on the pasture lands. They tended the calves along with the other boys. While the calves grazed, they would romp around on the cool grass and play. games.

One day they had taken the calves to the pastures. A wicked asura who wanted to kill them, assumed the form of a calf (*Vatsa*), and mingled with the rest of the herd. Krishna saw this and pointed it out to Balarama. Quietly, he sneaked up on the calf from behind and caught it by the hind legs. He whirled it round and round and dashed it against a *kapittha* tree. The animal died and at once its body turned into an awful rakshasa. The *gopa* boys cheered loudly. Krishna was the hero of the day.

In the dark woods, Krishna and the *gopas* had gone to a tank to quench their thirst and to have a cool wash. When they came out, they saw before them what looked like a huge white mountain. It was, in fact, an asura in the form of a monstrous crane. The monster now rushed at Krishna and held him fast in his beak. The *gopas* panicked at the sight and some of them fainted. The crane called Bakasura, had been sent by Kamsa to destroy Krishna.

Now Krishna generated so much heat with his body that it began to scorch the throat of the asura. The Baka (crane) suddenly spat out the divine boy and made another attack on him with its sharp beak. Krishna pressed down the beak of the giant bird with his foot and with his hands he tore it apart. The asura fell down dead. The devas who were watching the fight were greatly pleased. They beat their celestial drums and blew their conches and showered heavenly flowers upon Krishna. The *gopas* were soon revived and embraced Krishna affectionately. Back in Vrindavana, they told their elders the story of how Krishna had killed the demon, Bakasura. They were indeed very pleased that the boy had been saved from the jaws of death, but not understanding his

Bala Bhagavatam

तस्मापत्नन्तं स निगृह्ण रुक्ष्यो—
र्दोर्भ्यो बकं कंससखं सतां पति: ।
पश्यत्सु बालेषु ददार लीलया
मुधावहो वीरणवद्विवोकसम् ॥

(स्क. 10 अ. 11 श्लो. 51)

The Lord of the Virtuous, catching the beaks of the Baka-Asura, a friend of Kamsa, and while other cow-boys were watching, as though in play:
He tore the bird into two halves.
Bala Krishna kills Bakasura

divine nature, they could not explain how Krishna managed to escape from every danger that he was subjected to.

AGHASURA VADHAM

One day Krishna desired to have breakfast in the forest. He rose early in the morning and played on his flute. The *gopas* heard the sweet melody and woke up too. They came out of their houses in thousands, their calves following them.

They were truly in high spirits as they made their way to the forest. Some *gopas* played their flutes and some blew their horns. Some hummed like the bees and some cooed like the *kokilas*. Some chased the shadows of birds, others imitated the graceful gait of swans, still others stood still like storks and some danced the proud dance of the peacocks. Some *gopas* pulled the tails of monkeys and climbed trees after them; they pulled faces like them and jumped from tree to tree after them. It was all tremendous fun. They skipped and romped about. They playfully wrestled and joked and chattered ceaselessly. They teased and raced and laughed and sang. And not one of them was aware of the danger that lay ahead of them!

There was a demon called Agha who was the younger brother of Poothana and Bakasura. He was fully determined to avenge their deaths. He swore to himself that he would kill Krishna and all the laughing, chattering *gopas*. Agha stretched himself in the form of a huge python, one Yojana long. He opened wide his mouth. His lower jaw rested on the earth and his upper jaw touched the clouds. He lay quite still, and waited patiently for the *gopas* to draw near.

When the *gopas* came near the waiting asura, they playfully started speculating about the nature of the huge monstrosity before them. Some said it was a colossal serpent, others said it was the goddess of Vrindavana, and yet others said it was just a geographical feature of the forest. Then they said, "So what if it is a serpent? We will surely be saved from it like we were saved from the crane, Baka." So saying, they walked straight into the mouth of the serpent. They clapped their hands joyfully and bubbling with laughter, they, with the calves, walked along the tongue of the villainous asura, thinking it to be a smooth, bread road!

Now Krishna had known of this death-trap. But he had no time to warn his companions, so engrossed were they in their merry-making. The demon Aghasura did not immediately close his mouth, because his main aim was to kill Krishna. Krishna pondered for a while as to what would be the best course to take. After a moment or two, he himself entered the mouth of the giant serpent. Carefully, he wedged himself in Aghasura's throat preventing him from breathing. Aghasura choked and then breathed his last. With great speed, Krishna brought his friends out and saved them just as they were about to be consumed by the demon's "gastric-fire." The devas again rejoiced and burst forth into songs in praise of the Lord. Kamsa, the scheming fiend, found himself in deep distress. His evil intentions had again been defeated.

84

Bala Bhagavatam

उत्थायोत्थाय कृष्णस्य चिरस्य पादयोः पतन् ।
आस्ते महित्व प्रारदृष्ट स्मृत्वा समृत्वा पुन: पुन: ॥

(स्क. 10 अ. 13 श्लो. 63)

अनुजानीहि मा कृष्ण! सर्वं त्वं वेत्सि सर्वदृक् ।
त्वमेव जगता नाथो जगदेतत्त्वयिस्थितम् ॥

(स्क. 10 अ. 14 श्लो. 39)

Again and again Brahmaji (Creator) did prostrations, seeing the glory of the Lord's Maya, again and again. "Lord Krishna! I knew it not. Thou art the Omniscient! You know everything. Thou art the Lord of the Universe. The whole Universe rests in Thee only.
Brahmaji Prostrates to Bala Krishna

But it so happened that the story reached Vraja only a year later. This is how it happened.

BRAHMAJI'S MOHA BHANGAM

After the killing of Agha, Krishna and the *gopas* went to the river banks. They were hungry, and the hour was late. Each boy took out his own packet of food. They all sat in a circle and Krishna sat in their midst. While they were thus engrossed in eating their food, the cattle strayed away along the river bank. After some time, the *gopa* boys missed their cattle and wore worried frowns on their faces. They got up to search for them. But Krishna said, "No, don't bother. Sit down and finish your meal. I will go and look for them. I'll soon be back." So the boys went back to their meal and Krishna went to look for the missing calves.

Now Brahmaji had witnessed Krishna's tricks and his extraordinary strength and prowess. He felt a longing to experience Krishna's powers for himself. So in a moment of mischief, he hid all the calves in a mountain cave. Krishna searched high and low, in the forests, the hills and the valleys. But nowhere could he find even a trace of the calves. So he returned to the river bank to report the matter to the *gopas*. There, to his utter astonishment, he found the *gopas* missing too! What was he to make of these strange disappearances? He meditated deeply and then came to know that it was all a trick of Brahmaji to test his divinity. He smiled and decided that he would please Brahma and at the same time give an infinite experience of bliss to the mothers of the *gopas* and to the cows.

So he multiplied himself and assumed the forms of the *gopas* and their tender calves. He assumed their exact size, the exact number of hands and feet, holding an equal number of staves, horns and flutes, wearing the same clothes and then He, in his different forms, copied to the last detail, their individual behaviours, qualities, names, appearances, ages, voices, even their characteristic movements!

When it was dusk and the sun was preparing to set for the night, Krishna, and all the Krishna-*gopas* and the Krishna-calves wended their way back to their homes. When the mothers heard the sound of the flutes and the horns, they came running out to embrace their children. They hugged the boys close to their hearts, and fed them with tremendous joy. The cows too, showed more tenderness towards their calves. Vrindavana was bathed in ecstatic love.

The Lord, who is the essence of all beings, thus received the love of many thousand human and animal mothers. He, in turn, filled their devoted hearts with supreme bliss which arises from a total all-consuming love. Nobody noticed any change, except that the mothers started loving their boys more and more. Krishna, along with the mind-born Krishna-*gopas* and Krishna-calves would every morning go to the forest as usual. Every house, every family in Vraja was filled with an atmosphere of the highest kind of love. And thus the days passed till almost a year was over.

One day as the cows were grazing on the summit of Govardhana, they felt a tremendous upsurge of love for their calves, which were grazing near Vraja. Breathlessly, the cows rushed down the hillside to the calves. Balarama was watching all this and he thought, "Never have I seen the cows display such great love towards their calves. Even the mothers love the *gopas* more than they ever did." Then addressing Krishna, he said, "These calves and their keepers, the bow-herd boys, have all started looking like you, Krishna. What is the mystery? I am baffled." Krishna then explained to him all that had happened.

Brahma now became curious to see how Krishna had met the tricky situation he had put him into. So he mounted his swan and went to see. And lo! a more puzzled person there never was. For before him he saw two sets of *gopas* and their calves – one lot which he had imprisoned in the caves and one lot which was, as usual, tending the animals in the forest.

Just as a hazy darkness disappears in the total darkness of the night, just as the light of the glow-worm disappears in the light of the morning sun, so too, Brahmaji's *maya* seemed to have disappeared in the overpowering *maya* of Bhagavan! Brahma had been caught by his own *maya*. He was dazed and confused. Suddenly the haze before his eyes lifted, and he saw the *gopas* and the calves assuming the dark complexion of Krishna. Then he saw them all in the form of Sri Vishnu, four-armed, holding the divine conch, discus, mace and lotus, beaming with resplendent glory. The confusion now cleared and he understood what had happened. Brahmaji then alighted from his swan and bowing deeply, prostrated before Krishna. Then he rose and offered praise to the Lord. Brahmaji went thrice around Krishna, mounted his swan and disappeared and along with him also disappeared the Krishna-*gopas* and the Krishna-calves.

Under the trees were now sitting the original boys, and their calves were grazing not far away. Krishna joined them for the meal and laughingly showed them the corpse of the python which he had "only an hour ago killed!"

As evening drew near, the *gopas* picked their way back to Vraja. There they related to the elders how Krishna had killed Aghasura. They remembered nothing of what had happened to them meanwhile, since they had been under Brahmaji's spell. Only Krishna and Balarama knew the whole story and they kept it secret. The people of Vraja treasured all of Krishna's deeds in their memories and turned them into songs. And yet they remained ignorant of his divine nature!

DHENUKASURA VADHAM

सदैव पादपङ्कजं मदीयमानसे निजं
    दधानमुत्तमालकं नमामि नन्दबालकम् ।
समस्तदोषशोषणं समस्तलोकपोषणं
    समस्तगोपमानसं नमामि नन्दलालसम् ॥

"I bow to the Child of Nanda, Who has kept His lotus-feet in the beautiful pond of my devoted heart; and Who has lovely tresses. I bow to the Child after Whom Nanda is mad with love, Who destroys all sins, Who protects the whole universe, and Who is the very heart of cowherds."

Krishna had killed Aghasura when he was just five years old. With his fifth year began his *Paugandavayah**.

At this stage in the story we find that everyone is irresistibly attracted towards Krishna, more than ever before. It is the nature of the human mind to adore beauty in whatever form it is conceived. The five sense-organs as well as the mind and the intellect are thrilled by the individual beauties they are capable of perceiving. Thus the eyes can sense the beauty of perfect form and colour. The inner ear reacts joyously to melodious and sweet music. The tongue registers the beauty of taste. A beautiful fragrance is perfect beauty for the nose. And the ripples of a cool breeze, the warm embrace of loving ones, are beauty to the skin. Similarly, the mind adores the altar of beautiful poetry and noble sentiments, and the intellect pays homage to the sheer brilliancy of the thoughts of the masters of this world.

Whenever we see beauty – whether it be the physical beauty of a person, or a marvellous artist, or a world-famous musician, whether it be the best dancer or the best scientist, the best cook or the best philosopher – we cannot but help admire them for the extraordinary expression of their individual beauties.

If people are thus loved and respected the world over for even *one* great quality that they may possess, what then would be the condition of one who has ALL these qualities? Such then was the case with Krishna. He had the most charming physical appearance which endeared him at once to all his devotees. From the Bhagawad Geeta we know that he was the greatest philosopher, thinker, poet and musician. There was not a single quality which this divine boy did not possess. What wonder then that he was the dearly beloved of all the people of his time? (There were, of course, exceptions like Kamsa, who were so steeped in ignorance that they could not look at anything beautiful beyond their own vanity).

Krishna was thus dear to his parents because he was dutiful and obedient. His friends loved him because of his friendly nature and cheerfulness. The neighbours loved him because he protected them from all dangers. The *gopis* loved him for the beauty and the divinity of his very being. And the Rishis and sages loved him because he had achieved victory over his senses. Krishna was undoubtedly the darling of all.

× × ×

Time passed, and the boys grew older. Now they took the cattle for grazing to the rich pasturelands of Vrindavana. The grass was thick and green. Wild fruit and flowers grew in abundance. There were many lakes and ponds. And the silvery Yamuna wound her way strolling gently through the forest.

---

* (कुमार) *kumara* – boy below five years.

(पौगण्ड) *Pauganda* – boyhood from fifth to sixteenth year.

Bala Bhagavatam

कृष्ण: कदम्बमधिरुह्य ततोऽतिदूरं गा-
मास्फोट्यात गाढरशनो न्यपतद्विषोदे ॥

(स्क. 10 अ. 16 श्लो. 6)

Krishna then got up on the tall *Kadamba*-tree, and tightening His girdle, He clapped His hands, and dived into the poisoned waters of the pond.

Bala Krishna Prepares to fight Kaliya

Krishna and Balarama were drunk with the beauty of Vrindavana. Krishna loved to tickle his flute to divine melody, to dance with the peacocks, to imitate the cries of the jungle birds, and to entertain all his friends with a thousand pranks. When tired, he would rest his head on the lap of a *gopa* and would lie down on the soft green grass.

Some distance away from where the boys usually played, there was a beautiful palmyra garden. The *gopas* would watch the juicy Tala-fruits fall to the ground and rot away. They dared not go and pick the fruit, because in the garden lived a ferocious herd of asses, headed by an asura called Dhenukasura. They would never allow a human being to enter the garden. But the boys longed to eat the juicy fruit and pleaded with Krishna and Rama to help them get it.

Krishna and Balarama entered the garden. Balarama went up to the trees and shook them mightily, till the ground was covered with the Tala-fruits. Dhenukasura heard the noise and was incensed with anger. He charged at Balarama and struck his chest with his hind-legs. Then he turned and brayed and made ready for a second attack. Meantime, Balarama seized the ass's hind-legs which had been raised to strike and whirling it round and round in the air, hurled it against a tree. The asura hit the tree with such force, that it crashed into another. The second tree crashed into a third till a heap of trees lay on the ground. Now the other asses charged at the two brothers. But soon they too were killed one by one by Balarama and Krishna. From then onwards, the garden was free for the romp and play of the cow-herd boys.

KALIYA MARDANAM

In one part of the river Kalindi, there was a pool which was contaminated by the presence of a hundred-hooded serpent called Kaliya. The monster had been living in the pool with his family for many *yugas*. He constantly breathed poisonous fumes which kept the water at boiling point. All the birds that flew over that area were instantly killed, as was any other life that even came near it.

One day, the *gopas* with their cattle strayed to that very same part of the river Kalindi. The boys and the cattle were both thirsty. So they bent over the banks of the river to refresh themselves. No sooner had they drunk the water, than they fell down dead. Krishna, with his divine look, gazed upon them. They soon revived, but Krishna decided that once and for all he would do away with this poisonous serpent.

So while the *gopas* watched aghast, Krishna climbed a *kadamba* tree nearby. He removed his yellow *pitambara*, his peacock crown, his garland of wild flowers and placed them with his stick on a branch of the tree. Then he tightened his loin cloth and plunged into the boiling water. So great was the impact of his jump, that the water rose many yards high. Kaliya was vastly surprised and angered to see that someone had actually dared disturb his privacy. In his uncontrollable rage and fury Kaliya attacked Krishna fiercely and stung him with his fangs. Then he twined himself around the divine boy's tender body in order to cut him into small pieces. The *gopa* boys could bear to see no more. They felt that Krishna's death was now certain. They fell down in sorrow, senseless, and the cows wept and lowed in deep distress. Likewise, there were evil omens in Vraja. Nanda was greatly alarmed. The elders connected this somehow with Krishna as had been their habit in the past. They became even more worried as that day Balarama had not accompanied Krishna. Nanda and Yasoda, along with a large number of men, women and children went out in search of him, following the hoof-marks of the cows. On arriving at the spot where the struggle was going on, they saw the boys lying in a swoon and Krishna in the throes of death. The women screamed and fainted. The men wept and lamented. Yasoda went crazy with grief and Nanda prepared to jump into the water. Balarama, who alone was not affected because he knew the true nature of things, restrained Nanda and stopped him from acting rashly.

It was now an hour since Krishna had been in the grip of the awful demon. When he saw the distress of the people on the banks of the river, Krishna inflated himself to such a huge size that Kaliya lost his grip and could no longer hold him. Krishna now danced around him and, a little fatigued, the serpent also moved with him. Krishna then leaped onto the outspread hoods of Kaliya and broke them one by one. Kaliya was furious and hissed loudly. Fire and poison issued from his mouth and nostrils, and he twisted and twirled to free himself of Krishna. But Krishna continued dancing on his head and breaking the hoods. The sight was indeed very beautiful. The devas sang in joy and showered flowers from heaven. Soon, Kaliya was exhausted by his own struggles. He vomitted black blood and then swooned away, his body completely broken. For Krishna had danced on him with the weight of the three worlds!

Seeing their husband in a death-like swoon, the chaste wives of Kaliya approached Krishna and earnestly prayed for his life, and worshipped the Lord with deep devotion.* Krishna spared Kaliya's life and when he had fully regained consciousness, he humbly begged his pardon. He said, "O Lord of the Universe! Jagadeeswara! We who are steeped in *tamas* are vicious by nature. This we cannot overcome without Your Grace. Please show us this Grace or punish us as You think fit."

Krishna said, "Go Kaliya, with your wife and children. Go and live on Ramanaka Dvipa**. Leave these waters free for human beings and animals. Garuda, of whom

---

*नमस्तुभ्यं भगवते पुरूषाय महात्मने ।
भूतावासाय भूताय पराय परमात्मने ॥१॥
ज्ञानविज्ञाननिधये ब्रह्मणेऽनन्तशक्तये ।
अगुणायाविकाराय नमस्तेऽप्राकृताय च ॥२॥
कालाय कालनाथाय कालावयवसाक्षिणे ।
विश्वाय तदुपद्रष्ट्रे तत्कर्त्रे विश्वहेतवे ॥३॥
नमोऽनन्ताय सूक्ष्माय कूटस्थाय विपश्चिते ।
नानावादानुरोधाय वाच्यवाचकशक्तये ॥४॥
नमः कृष्णाय रामाय वसुदेवसुतायच ।
प्रद्युम्नायानिरुद्धाय सात्वतां पतये नमः ॥५॥
अव्याकृतविहाराय सर्वव्याकृतसिद्धये ।
हृषिकेश नमस्तेऽस्तु मुनये मौनशीलिने ॥६॥

you are mortally scared since he is your sworn enemy, will not harm you, because your hoods bear My foot marks. Go and live in peace!"

Kaliya, with his entire family, left for Ramanaka Dvipa as commanded by Krishna. Ever since then the waters of the Yamuna have been pure and sweet.

When Krishna came out of the water, he was wearing rare gems and jewels and his body was smeared with sandal paste. These gifts were given to him by the wives of Kaliya. The people of Vraja embraced Krishna and they shed tears of joy. The cows and their calves were seen frisking about instinctively in their inexplicable delight. Yasoda hugged him again and again and Nanda distributed gifts to one and all.

The people of Vraja were, by now, extremely tired due to the intense activities of the day. So they decided to spend the night on the banks of the river. When they were resting at night, a fire broke out in the forest on account of the great summer heat. The *gopas* and *gopis* were woken up by the scorching flames and ran to Krishna, begging him to save them. Krishna drew near, swallowed the fire, and wiped out all signs of the destruction wrecked by it.

Slowly, the seasons changed. Summer passed into the rainy season, the rains passed into autumn, and autumn into winter. And once again it was summer. One day, Krishna and his companions had gone to a distant forest driving their cattle before them. The summer sun was fierce and the day was very hot. Krishna and the cowboys found shelter under the cool shade of a tree. To his companions, Krishna said, "Look, friends. How noble these trees are. Truly, they live for others. They themselves bear the tortures of wind, rain, sun and frost but offer protection to others from them. In the service of living beings, they offer their all— leaves, flowers, fruits, shade, roots, bark, fragrance, their juice, their ashes, fuel, buds and everything. Of all beings living on this earth, only they justify their birth who use whatever they have in the service of their fellow-beings, they be wealth or wisdom."

---

1. *My devoted prostrations unto Him, Who dwells in my body, Who is ever-gracious, Who is the Self in all, Who is present in all creatures, Whose form is the whole Universe with all beings in it, incomparable, to Him Who is the Supreme Truth – again my prostrations.

2. To Him Who is a treasure of true Wisdom, Who has infinite power, Who never changes, Who is beyond all qualities, Who is in Nature ever present, playing His own games – to Him my devoted prostrations.

3. One, Who is the nature of Time, One Who whirls and turns Time, One, Who is the axle around which Time revolves, One, Who is a witness watching the flood of Time – One Who is of the Universal Form, One Who "watches" the play of the Universe, Who is the one Creator, Who is the cause of everything in this world – to Him my devoted prostrations.

4. To Him, Who is endless, supremely subtle, changeless, Knower-of-everything, Who is present in all speech and discussion, Who is the very Power of meaning in words – to Him my devoted prostrations.

5. O Lord Krishna! I salute Thee Who art the Son of Vasudeva, Who art the very heart of Balarama; I salute Thee Who art both Pradyumna and Aniruddha, Who art the Lord of all devotees – Thee I salute.

6. To Him Who plays about in the "unseen-secret-space", Who expresses through all the wondrous things of the manifest world, Who is the silent Sage of Wisdom, Who silently watches all thoughts within us – to Him – to Hrishikesha – my devoted prostrations.

** Dvipa – Island.

Bala Bhagavatam

चतुर्विधं बहुगुणमभमादाय भाजनें : ।
श्रमिसस्त्रः प्रियं सर्वैः समुद्रमिव निम्नगाः ॥

(स्क. 10 अ. 30 श्लो. 19)

The Brahmin Ladies, carrying prepared food, of all four kinds, in plenty, rushed to the Lord from all sides, as rivers gush towards the ocean.

The Brahmin Ladies Bring Food for Bala Krishna

KRISHNA AND THE BRAHMIN WOMEN

Thus, engaged in conversation, Krishna and the *gopas* passed from the shade of one tree to another till they arrived at the banks of the river. The cows and the boys plunged into the river to refresh themselves. By the time they came out they had worked up a tremendous appetite. So they asked Krishna and Balarama to find them something to eat. Krishna remembered that not far away there were some Brahmin women who were devotees of Sri Hari and whose husbands were at the time engaged in performing a Yagna. He instructed them to go to these Brahmins and to beg of them some cooked food in the name of Krishna and Balarama. The *gopas* went to the Brahmins and with folded hands asked them to spare some food for Krishna and his companions. But the Brahmins paid no heed. They were intent on completing the Yagna from which they hoped to gain some small merits.

The disappointed *gopas* came back to Krishna and reported to him their failure in getting food. Krishna laughed and asked them to go back to the Brahmin ladies. They, when they heard that Krishna was in the nighbourhood, could not wait to get there to see him. They tastefully arranged the food on golden platters, and ignoring the protests of their husbands, sons, brothers and friends, they hurried to the place where Krishna waited with his companions. When they saw the Blue Boy clad in yellow silk, the peacock feather in a coronet of tender leaves on his head, decked with fresh water-lilies and a garland of wild flowers, they felt a tremendous upsurge of love for him. The Brahmin ladies then embraced Krishna and fed him lovingly. Krishna smiled at their devotion and said gently, "Welcome, O noble-minded ladies! You have, overcome all obstacles in order to come and meet Me, who am in truth, your *Atman*, your innermost Self. Nothing in the world can be dearer than the *Atman*. Because of the *Atman* it is that husband, wife, relative and friend are dear. Now that you have seen Me, go back to your husbands and help them to end their Yagna successfully."

The Brahmin ladies said, "Lord, do not be so cruel. We have left our homes and husbands, we have cut off all attachments, that we may come and serve You, that we may adorn our heads with the *Tulasi* thrown from Your feet. Even if we now return, we will not be accepted by our husbands and our brothers. Therefore, Lord, grant us refuge at Your feet."

But Krishna replied with great love and compassion, "Your husbands and friends cannot find fault with you, since My favour is upon you. It is not necessary that direct contact alone enhances love and devotion. By keeping your mind fixed on Me constantly, you shall attain My Being.*

---

*पतयो नाभ्यसूयेरन् पितृभ्रातृसुतादयः ।
लोकाश्च वो मयोपेता देवा अप्यनुमन्वतु ॥
न प्रीतयेऽनुरागाय ह्यङ्गसङ्गो नृणामिह ।
तन्मनो मयि युञ्जाना अचिरान्मामवाप्स्यथ ॥

The Brahmin women prostrated to Krishna and went back to their homes and husbands. They were well received, and the husbands, seeing the boundless devotion of their wives, themselves began worshipping Krishna.

INDRA YAGNA BHANGAM

The rainy season was drawing near and in Vraja, there were great preparations for a Yagna going on. Krishna approached his father respectfully and asked, "What is all this about, father? In whose honour is this sacrifice being performed? What will be its outcome?"

Nanda said, "Son, Indra is the god of clouds and rain. Rain gives life to all beings. Therefore Indra is to be worshipped. Besides, we have to respect the tradition which has come down to us from our forefathers."

Krishna replied, "Why do you talk about thanking Indra? The birth and death of men are pre-ordained according to their *karma*. Where does Indra come in when people are governed by their own *karma*? Each being lives and acts according to his own essential nature. We do not live in towns and cities. We live in the forests. The cows are our means of livelihood, they are our wealth. Let us then worship them. Let us worship the Govardhana mountain with its green grass and rich pasturelands. With the preparations already made, let the Brahmins offer sacrifice to the cows, the mountain and to Me. Whatever remains, let us distribute it to everyone, even down to the down-trodden dogs and *pariahas.*"

Nanda and all the elders thought this an excellent suggestion. So then Indra did not get his usual worship. It was the cows and the Govardhana-mount which received the adoration of the people of Vraja.

Now Indra became terribly jealous and angry. He made up his mind to seek revenge. He sent forth his clouds and winds which were generally kept in reserve for doomsday, (*mahapralaya*).

He instructed them to wreck havoc on Vrindavana and to destroy the land and people completely. He promised to be on their side, astride his magnificent white-elephant, (*Airavata*) in the company of the wind-god (*Vayu-Deva*).

The clouds were released from their chains. There was thunder and lightning the like of which had never been seen on earth. Rain poured down in continuous sheets. There were thunderstorms and hail-storms. Water flooded into every house, hut shelter and cow-shed. Human beings and animals became blue with cold and looked as though they would die. The extreme dampness and cold made their knees knock and their teeth chatter. The people were in great distress. Not only were their houses destroyed, even their food was spoiled. There was nothing for them to eat. Their children looked frozen and pinched with hunger.

At last the *gopis* took their babies to Krishna and pleaded with him to save them from the anger of Indra. Krishna was moved when he saw their plight. He lifted Govardhana with one hand and called all the people to take shelter under it.

For seven days it rained without stop. For seven days Krishna held aloft the Govardhana mountain while the people took refuge under it.

Indra was puzzled and surprised. When he realised how futile was his anger and jealousy, he grew ashamed and withdrew the clouds and the wind. The sun came out and shone brightly. The floods subsided, the land became dry once again and the river's flow became calm and clear. The people of Vraja came out and went back to their old places and Krishna replaced the hill. The *gopis* showered on him unbroken rice and rained flowers and blessings on him.

The news of Krishna's feats soon spread. The elders of the clan got together and marvelled at the superhuman achievements of the young boy. They remembered all his deeds from infancy onwards and spoke of their wonder to Nanda. It was then that Nanda told them that Garga had identified the boy with Sri Narayana at the naming ceremony. The *gopas* accepted the divinity of Krishna and worshipped him as the Lord of the Universe.

By this time, Indra too had come to his senses. Very apologetically, he approached the Lord and prostrated before Him. He touched His feet and begged His pardon.*

Krishna said, "All this was done to break your pride, Indra. I take away the powers of those whom I want to favour. Go now and perform your duties faithfully."

Surabhi, the divine mother of all cows also came down and worshipped Krishna. She bathed Him with her milk, and Indra and the other gods bathed Him with the waters of the Akashaganga. And they all called him GOVINDA. The Rishis, siddhas, gandharvas and vidyadharas, all rejoiced at the holy ceremony. The three worlds were filled with joy. Everyone felt the holy presence of the Lord and found himself blessed.

---

*नमस्तुभ्यं भगवते पुरुषाय महात्मने ।
वासुदेवाय कृष्णाय सात्वतां पतये नमः ॥१॥
स्वच्छन्दोपात्तदेहाय विशुद्धज्ञानमूर्तये ।
सर्वस्मै सर्वबीजाय सर्वभूतात्मने नमः ॥२॥
त्वयेशानुगृहीतोऽस्मि ध्वस्तस्तम्भो वृथोद्यमः ।
ईश्वरं गुरुमात्मानं त्वामहं शरणं गतः ॥३॥

1.   My devoted prostrations to Thee – Who art the Lord dwelling in the city of my body, Who art the Great Life present everywhere – to Thee, O Son of Vasudeva, Lord of the Sattwatas, – to Thee Lord Krishna, my devoted prostrations.

2.   To Him, Who has His body under perfect control, Whose nature is pure Wisdom, in Whom is everything, Who is the "seed" for the entire Universe, Who is the Self in every being – to Him my devoted prostrations.

3.   Blessed am I! I have become humble and have left all my improper efforts! I have taken shelter under Thy protection – Who art the Lord, the World-Teacher, the very *atman* in all!

रन्ध्रान् वेणोरधरसुधया पूरयन् गोपवृन्दै—
वृन्दारण्यं स्वपदरमणं प्राविशाद्गीतकीर्तिः ।   (स्क. 10 अ. 21 श्लो. 5)

Along with all the other cowherd boys, Lord Krishna entered for his play the plains of Brindavan, filling the holes of his flute with the nectar of his lips.

Sri Krishna, Lord of Love & Life

RASA LEELA

It was a full moon night in autumn. The moon-beams bathed the forest in their silvery light. The heat of the day had vanished and every flower, every blade of grass in the cool forest of Vrindavana shimmered in the moon's heavenly light. The Yamuna was singing sweetly by, and the soft white petals of the lilies had trembled open. A gentle breeze came over the dale, wafting the fragrance of freshblown jasmine. Peace had descended on Vraja and most of the people were already asleep.

Krishna, Lord of Love and Life, was enchanted by the beauty of the night. Flute in hand he was sitting all alone on the bank of the murmuring Yamuna. He raised the flute to his lips and the air was filled with the divinest melody. The soft notes carried the burden of heavenly music to the hushed houses of Vraja. The *gopis* heard the full rich sound of the divine Flute-Player, and were seized with an intense longing to see the Lord of their hearts, the Lord of the Universe. At the time they were all engaged in various tasks in their houses. Some were closing up the cow-sheds, some were settling for the night, some were feeding their babies, some were boiling the milk, some were serving food to their elders and some were serving their husbands.

But a divine call can never be ignored. When the soul is stirred by the divine music of the Lord's flute, then all worldly chores and activities drop off all by themselves. When once a devotee has experienced intense love and longing for the Lord, the duties of the world seem meaningless and they slide into the background. So when they heard the sound of the flute, the *gopis* dropped whatever work they were engaged in, and gathering their swirling skirts about them, they rushed to the banks of the holy river Yamuna.

Krishna saw the *gopis* as they neared him and laughed as he saw them stumble and trip and race in their anxiety to reach him first. Mischievously, he asked them, "Fair ladies. What can I do for you? What have you all come here for, forsaking your elders and husbands and children? This is not the time when young ladies should be out, away from the fires of their hearths. I know fully your great devotion to Me. This you can increase by constantly meditating upon Me and singing My divine glories. Now go back to your homes, to your husbands and children."

The *gopis* had not expected the Lord to banish them from His company. They said to Him, "All wise people, the world over, constantly find bliss in You, Who are the Eternal Self in all. Who in the three worlds can compare with You? You are the fountain of bliss for Your devotees. Where can one find pleasure more than that of Your own divine company? What meaning then, do husbands, children and relatives have? Lord, if You force us to go, our legs heavier than lead, will refuse to carry us home. Our hands will refuse to work. Our minds will know no peace. Then Lord, we will truly have to totally renounce home and husband and, like Rishis and Yogis, we will have to seek You in the silence of meditation. Therefore, please be kind to us and let us remain for some time in Your company divine."

Krishna smiled. He was touched by their sincerity and deep devotion. So he took them to the riverside. There the *gopis* sang and danced, in the moonlight around the Flute-bearer. Soon, however, Krishna noticed that the *gopis* had become proud of their good fortune in being with him. So, to teach them a lesson, he vanished from their midst. The *gopis*, now tired and fatigued, missed Krishna. They became distressed and lamented loudly at this loss. They were like a herd of deer which had lost its leader. Now they roamed in and out of the forest, searching for their Lord. Some asked the trees, with tears in their eyes, whether they had seen Krishna. Some asked the creepers, some asked the birds, and others the deer. They were disconsolate with grief. Where, O where had their Krishna gone, leaving them thus so forlorn and alone?*

When Krishna felt the *gopis* had been sufficiently punished for their arrogance, he suddenly appeared in their midst. The *gopis* were so delighted to see him again that they caught his hands and led him to a seat which they prepared with their soft veils. Then Krishna spoke to them of the difference between selfish and unselfish love. He acknowledged that their love for him was pure and unselfish, and assured them that their total devotion for him would be amply rewarded.

Then, in the light of the full moon, Krishna and the *gopis* started the *Rasa* dance. Krishna multiplied himself in such a way, that in the *Rasa* circle, there was an apparent Krishna between every two *gopis*, so that every *gopi* felt that the Lord was nearest to her. All the celestials came in their heavenly chariots to witness this unique dance between the Lord and His devotees. They brought along their musical instruments and drums and felt delighted, indeed blessed, to be able to witness the Lord's play. As the strings stirred under the fingers of the heavenly musicians, and the drums sounded rich and deep, the *Rasa* dance started with measured steps and perfect rhythm. The bangles and anklets of the *gopis* jingled and tinkled to the rhythm, their limbs swayed and their skirts swirled with an unearthly beauty. The pace of the dance slowly quickened and soon the dance had developed a quality of great ecstasy and divine fervour. Then, as the dance came to an end, Krishna, followed by the *gopis* entered the cool waters of the Yamuna. They emerged after a refreshing bath. By that time it was *Brahma-muhurta***, and the *gopis* reluctantly, though still filled with divine ecstasy, made their way home.

How wonderful was this love the *gopis* had for the Lord of Vrindavana! How beautiful in its utter simplicity! How innocent and child-like in its complete lack of self-consciousness! The *gopis* are the *sattwic* devotees, their minds always fixed on their Self, Krishna. As the needle in the compass always seeks the north, so too the minds of the *gopis* were always turning to the lotus feet of the Lord.

---

*हा नाथ रमण प्रेष्ठ क्वासि क्वासि महाभुज ।
दास्यास्ते कृपणाया मे सखे दर्शय सन्निधिम् ॥

O Lord! O Blissful One! Where, O where are You? O mighty – armed One? O my Friend, show Yourself to me – I am Your forlorn slave!

** auspicious hour before dawn.

Let us then dwell deeply and meditate upon this marvellous *leela* of the Lord, this supreme Love between the devotees and their Beloved, that we too may rise above our lower tendencies and baser instincts.

तव कथामृतं तप्तजीवनं ।
कविभिरीडितं कल्मषापहम् ॥
श्रवणमङ्गलं श्रीमदाततं ।
भुवि गृणन्ति ते भूरिदा जनाः ॥

"O Krishna! Thy stories, sung by poets, give life to those who are burnt in worldly-sorrows. They destroy our sins. By merely listening to them we invoke auspiciousness. These stories sing Thy glories in every line. Great men ever repeat them and spread them in the world."

SALVATION OF SUDARSHANA

As years rolled by, Krishna grew to be a boy of twelve years. Nanda had taken a vow that when Krishna became twelve years of age, he would offer a special worship to the family goddess, Ambika. Along with neighbours and friends, Nanda went to the temple of the goddess with gifts of milk, curd, butter and milk-sweets. They were accompanied by men sounding drums and blowing trumpets. At the temple Nanda performed the sacred ritual in all its beauty. Then he fed the Mahatmas. By the time the worship and prayers were over, it had become dark. So they decided to spend the night in the temple court-yard.

Nanda and his followers lay down to rest. The night had advanced. The fires had sunk to smouldering embers. Suddenly, the party was woken up by a disturbed shout from Nanda. They re-lit their torches and saw that his foot was in the mouth of an unimaginably huge python. They beat the snake with sticks and thrust burning faggots into its body. But the snake would not leave its hold. It held on even more firmly and just would not let go. Nanda shouted to Krishna for help. Krishna rushed to his father's rescue. He touched the back of the snake with his foot. At once, the ugly python changed into a handsome and shining vidyadhara, who bowed low before Krishna with folded hands. Krishna asked him who he was. He replied, "My name is Sudarshana. I am a celestial magician. I had become very proud of my skill and beauty. One day I had gone to the forest in my chariot. There the Rishi Angira was sitting in deep meditation. I flew over him in my chariot a hundred times. Aroused from his meditation he cursed me into being a python, saying that I would be released from it by the grace of Krishna. That is why I came and seized Nanda's foot. Please forgive me." With deep prostration, he mounted his chariot and sped away to Suraloka.

SHANKHACHUDA

Once it so happened that the brothers Krishna and Balarama were in the forest with the *gopis*. The brothers sang and played their flutes and the *gopis* listened in rapt attention. Just then there came upon them a yaksha, a vile attendant of Kubera, the god of wealth. His name was Shankhachuda. He seized the unsuspecting *gopis* and drove

Bala Bhagavatam

स चुकोशाहिना ग्रस्त: कृष्ण ! कृष्ण ! महान्ययम्
सर्पो मांग्रासते तात ! प्रपन्नं परिमोच्य ॥ (स्क. 10 अ. 34 श्लो. 6)

Nanda cried out, "I am caught ! Krishna! Krishna! This big serpent has caught me, son! I surrender to Thee! Save me completely."

Salvation of Sudarshana Vidyadhara

them northwards. The girls wept and screamed for help. Krishna and Balarama uprooted a *sal* tree each and gave chase to the yaksha. Frightened of the brothers, Shankhachuda dropped the *gopis* and fled as fast as he could. "Brother, you look after them," cried Krishna and he sped after the fleeing yaksha. Soon, Shankhachuda was killed by a blow of Krishna's fist, and his crest-jewel, a precious gem, rolled down. Krishna picked it up and presented it lovingly to Balarama.

From then onwards, as of before, the *gopis* were constantly singing the glories of Krishna, their one Saviour, and with their minds fixed in an unbroken stream of thought on the Blue-Boy-of-Vrindavana they cheerfully went about their daily tasks and duties.

NARADA AND KAMSA

Now the time for Kamsa's death was fast approaching. Narada, the divine sage, who ever acts as the instrument to carry out Lord's wishes, went to Kamsa and said, "O Kamsa, you have been tricked. Devaki's eighth son still lives in the house of Nanda, in Vraja. The female child that you sought to kill was Yasoda's baby. The two were exchanged on the night of Krishna's birth. Krishna and his brother Balarama have killed all the asuras you sent to kill them."

Kamsa was terribly agitated and angered by this news. He drew out his sword and rushed to kill Vasudeva. But Narada stopped him and explained that Vasudeva was quite innocent. Nevertheless, Kamsa had Devaki and her husband put into chains and thrown into the darkest dungeons. Narada departed, and Kamsa sent for his ministers and counsellers.

To them he said, "Narada has just told me that the brothers Rama and Krishna, who will be the cause of my death are still alive. I will send for them both, and have them killed in a wrestling match. Prepare the play-grounds. The elephant Kuvalayapida will be placed at the entrance. He will kill my enemies. Arrange for a Dhanur-Yagna (bow-sacrifice) on the fourteenth day of the lunar month. Let us propitiate Shiva for our victory. Keep the elephant keepers and wrestlers ready." Thus he gave them minute instructions for the preparations.

Kamsa sent for Akroora, one of the chiefs of the Yadava clan. "Akroora, my dear friend," he said. "You are trusted wherever you go. Please go to Vraja. Take this chariot with you. Bring back the two sons of Vasudeva. Tell them that they have been invited by me to witness the Dhanur-Yagna and to see the sights of the town. My powerful elephant will kill the brothers, and if they, by any chance, escape him, my wrestlers will quickly do away with them. Then I will have Vasudeva, my father Ugrasena, his brother Devaka and all the Vrishnis, Bhojas and Dasharhas — all of them killed. The earth will be rid of all my foes. I will have on my side such stalwart asuras as Jarasandha, Samvara, Naraka and Bana. With their help I will rule the entire world. Hurry now with my message to Vraja. My wonderful plan cannot but succeed."

The wise Akroora replied, "Your plan is indeed wonderful, O Kamsa. But one must keep a balanced mind in success and in failure. Many times lofty plans are frustrated by unforeseen obstacles, causing us as much grief as their success would have caused us joy. Nevertheless, I will cary out your bidding."

AKROORA'S MESSAGE

Akroora was indeed very pleased that he had been chosen to convey the message to Vraja. His joy knew no bounds at the thought that at last he would see the lotus-feet of the Lord. He felt sure that despite the message he was carrying, the Lord would know of his deep devotion to Him and therefore would forgive him all his sins. All along the way to Vraja, his mind was absorbed in Krishna and he rehearsed in his mind how he would fall at his feet when he met him, how he would raise him and embrace him, etc.

Akroora reached Vraja just as the sun was setting. Krishna and Balarama, refreshed after a bath, were strolling in the courtyard, where the cows were being milked. There was a lovely fragrance of fresh sandal-paste about them and they wore neat clean clothes of blue and yellow. Gems sparkled at their throats and their chests were adorned with garlands of wild flowers. In great excitement at beholding the beautiful, shining face of the Lord, Akroora jumped down from his chariot. He was overwhelmed with joy. The tears rolled freely down his cheeks as he fell at the feet of Krishna and prostrated before him. His voice was choked with emotion which prevented him from saying who he was, where he had come from and for what purpose. Gently, Krishna raised him to his feet and embraced him warmly. Balarama too, embraced him and greeted him affectionately. Then the brothers took him inside. They made him comfortable. They washed his tired feet and massaged them and fed him a delicious meal. Then Nanda and Akroora exchanged greetings.

While they were talking, Akroora told them how Narada had come to Kamsa and revealed to him the secret of Krishna's birth. He also told them the real reason why he had been sent to Vraja. At this, Krishna and Balarama laughed heartily. Nanda ordered at once that the carriages and presents be got ready for their trip to Mathura. He had it proclaimed throughout Vraja that early the next morning they would proceed to Mathura to witness the great bow-sacrifice.

Next morning as the sun crept over the horizon, Akroora offered his prayers. The boys climbed on to his carriage. Slowly, the carriages and carts started moving towards Mathura. Akroora's chariot was followed by the chariots of Nanda and the other *gopas*. Behind them came the carts loaded with gifts of milk, curd and butter for Kamsa.

And the *gopis*? Who can describe the sorrow they felt at the separation from their Lord? Their hearts were numb and heavy with grief. They followed the carriages with heart-rending pleas. They wept and ran behind the chariots for a long distance. They bade the brothers farewell and for a long time watched after the carriages even after they had disappeared from sight. They felt limp and forlorn, like creepers whose support has been taken away. Back in Vraja, the *gopis* went about their work as usual but their minds were fixed on Krishna. When they were together they spoke of His deeds and glories and sang songs in His praise. When they were alone, they meditated deeply upon the Divine nature of the Lord.

MATHURA

नमस्ते वासुदेवाय सर्वभूतक्षयाय च ।
हृषिकेश नमस्तुभ्यं प्रपन्नं पाहि मां प्रभो ॥

"O Vasudeva! Thou art the One in Whom all beings merge back in the end; I salute Thee. O Hrishikesha ! I bow down to Thee in devotion. O Prabho ! Lord ! Protect me – I have surrendered to Thee. Give me harbour."

It was noon and the sun was right overhead. Akroora stopped the chariot on the bank of the Mandakini. The brothers refreshed themselves in the waters of the river and came back to the chariot. Akroora then requested their permission to go and bathe in the river and to perform his mid-day worship with the chanting of the *Gayatri Mantra*. As he was thus engaged in worship, he saw in the water Krishna and Balarama. He was astounded ! Why, only moments ago he had left them in the chariot. So he rushed back but beheld Rama and Krishna as he had left them sometime back, talking to each other! Speechless with wonder and amazement, he plunged into the river again. And lo! There he saw the thousand-headed serpent-king, Sesha, wearing a thousand crowns, stretched majestically in the water. On him lay Lord Vishnu, clad in yellow, resplendent with four arms. Around Him, worshipping Him in silent adoration stood the four Kumaras, the siddhas, gandharvas and Rishis, the Prajapatis and devotees like Prahlada and Narada, and a number of gods and goddesses. Akroora was awed by this glorious vision of the Lord. He folded his hands and prostrated in great devotion. Then, as a play is withdrawn from the stage, Krishna withdrew this form. Still full of the bliss of the vision, Akroora went back to the chariot.

Krishna was indeed amused when he saw the change in Akroora's face. He said, "Tell us, Uncle, what wonders have you seen in the water, sky or earth that you look so transformed?" And Akroora replied, "All the wonders in the water, sky and earth are only Yours. Having seen You I have indeed seen all the wonders of the world."

Akroora then drove fast his chariot so that by sundown they had reached the outskirts of Mathura. Humbly, he requested them to be his guests in Mathura, and offered praise to the Lord.

देव देव जगन्नाथ पुण्यश्रवणकीर्त्तन ।
यदूत्तमोत्तमश्लोक नारायण नमोऽस्तुते ॥

"O Lord Of Lords! The sole King of the Universe! One Who bestows merits on those who listen to and sing the glories of the Lord! O Krishna! Best among the Yadus! O Narayana! I bow down to Thee."

स्तुवतस्तस्य भगवान् दर्शयित्वा जले वपुः ।
भूयः समाहरत् कृष्णो नटी नाट्यमिवात्मनः ॥ (स्क.10अ.41श्लो.1)

For a moment Krishna gave his vision to his devotee Akroora in the very waters of Jamuna. As a dancer dancing for a moment on the stage and disappearing – the vision dissolved away.

Akroora sees the Divine Vision

Krishna and Balarama promised to come to his house once Kamsa had been killed. Sorrowfully, Akroora left them and went to inform Kamsa that the boys had arrived in the city.

Mathura was a beautiful city. The roads were broad and neat. The city was fortified and there was a moat running all around it. There were huge granaries, where all the grain was stored. There were beautiful parks and gardens, market-places, business houses and rest-houses. There were public shelters for weary travellers and the mansions were fine and huge. Krishna and Balarama were utterly delighted with everything they saw. They walked about in the streets. By this time everybody had come to know that Krishna and Balarama had arrived. The women and children rushed to their windows and balconies and craned their necks to catch a glimpse of the brothers. They showered flowers on them and felt blessed when they looked up and smiled at them. Every now and then, the people would step out into the streets sprinkled with water, and worship Rama and Krishna with incense and lamps, rice and curds, flowers and fruits.

As they went along, they passed a washerman's shop. Krishna requested him to give them the best of the fine clothes he had, and promised him great blessings in return. The washerman, however, worked for Kamsa and was arrogant. He said, "What! Do you get such fine clothes to wear in the mountains and forests where you roam? Be off, foolish boys, before the king's officers come and arrest you. Never make such demands again."

Lightly, Krishna touched his head with his fingertips. Instantly, the washerman's head was separated from his body. The servants saw this and ran here and there in great confusion. Krishna and Balarama chose the finest clothes for themselves and distributed the rest among the *gopas*.

Then they came across a weaver who lovingly dressed the boys with the best clothes he had and which made their complexions glow even more. Krishna blessed him for his devotion. The brothers now entered the house of a garland-maker called Sudama. Sudama worshipped them with betel leaves, garlands and flowers of all colours and fragrances. He prayed to the Lord for constant devotion and love for all His creatures. Krishna blessed him and conferred on him many boons and blessings.

Some time later, a young girl passed their way, carrying a pot of fragrant sandal-paste. She had a beautiful face which shone with kindness, but she had a hunchback. Krishna joked with her and said, "Tell me truly whom you carry this paste for. If you anoint us with it you will be suitably rewarded." The maid looked at their faces and answered pleasantly, "My name is Trivakra (one with three bends). I am a maid-servant. Every day I prepare this paste for Kamsa who likes it very much." Then with great love and devotion, she gave them the paste to smear on their neck and chest. As a reward, Krishna drew close to her and pressed her feet with his toes. He placed two of his fingers under her chin and lifted it. And lo! The hunchback straightened into a shapely young woman of great charm and beauty! In gratitude, she invited Krishna

रूपपेशल माधुर्यं हसितालाप वीक्षितैः ।
धर्षितात्मा ददौ सान्द्र मुभयोरनुलेपनम् ॥   (स्क. 10 अ. 42 श्लो. 4)

Fascinated by the smiling beauty of the sweet face of Krishna, unhesitatingly Trivakra offered her sandal paste to both of them.

Trivakra gives Chandan to Krishna and Rama

to come into her house. Krishna said, "I will certainly come when my work is over."

Krishna and Balarama visited all the places of interest in Mathura till they arrived at the sacrificial hall where the bow, huge and heavy and shining with the splendour of many precious gems, was kept on exhibition. People came and gazed at it with awe and reverence and placed by its side the many gifts and presents they had brought with them. The bow was heavily guarded by fierce-looking armed men. Krishna seized the bow before they could stop him and drew its string to his ear till it snapped into two! The snapping sounded like a terrific thunder-clap and reached the ears of Kamsa. It filled him with great fear and dread. The attendants of the bow rushed on Krishna and Balarama, bows and arrows in readiness. With nothing else in hand but one half of the bow each, the brothers killed the guards and other soldiers who sought to kill them. Then with a casual stride they walked out to complete their sight-seeing, and at nightfall, they reached their camp on the outskirts of the city.

DEATH OF KAMSA

* वसुदेवसुतं देवं कंसचाणूरमर्दनम् ।
देवकी परमानन्दं कृष्णं वन्दे जगद्गुरुम् ॥

Kamsa spent a sleepless night. He was extremely angry because his bow had been wrecked, because so many of his guards and soldiers had been killed, because his own special sandal-paste had been given to the boys from Vraja. All through the night he was disturbed by nightmares of death, torture and dishonour. When he looked into the mirror, he saw his body without a head! When he looked at the sky he saw every star double. His shadow appeared to be full of holes. When he walked, he left no footprints on the earth! In the midst of all these evil omens he tried to snatch some sleep. Then he dreamt that he was riding a donkey, that he had swallowed poison, that he was embraced by a dead relative, or that he was lying naked, his body smeared with oil. His nerves were on edge. He knew no rest or peace. He felt as though he was on the brink of madness.

At last, the sun rose over the eastern horizon. It was the day of the festival when the wrestling match was to take place. The vast arena of the amphitheatre was tastefully decorated with flowers, garlands and buntings. Spectators had started gathering from early morning in order to get seats at vantage points. The galleries were filled with princes and chiefs, ministers and traders, businessmen and priests. The wrestlers Chanura, Mustika, Kuta, Sala and Tosala – renowned the world over for their strength, prowess and skill in wrestling – had gathered, and were waiting for the matches to begin. At last, Kamsa arrived and took his seat on a raised platform. The trumpets blared forth, the drums sounded and the people cheered their king. This lifted the spirits of the

---

* I salute Lord Krishna – the divine son of Vasudeva, the destroyer of Kamsa and Chanura, the supreme bliss of Devaki, the Teacher of the Universe.

dejected king a little. Nanda and the *gopas* made their gifts and were given special seats to watch the matches.

After their morning bath, Krishna and Balarama strolled unhurriedly towards the amphitheatre. At the very entrance they were obstructed by the mighty elephant, Kuvalayapida. Krishna asked the mahout to remove the elephant, from their path. Instead, he urged the mighty beast to trample upon the two boys. The elephant moved forward and made to coil its trunk around Krishna. Krishna, however, slipped between the legs of the maddened beast and with a jump, caught its tail with both hands. He pulled it for twentyfive bow-lengths*, then whirled it round and round, mahout and all, and made it quite dizzy. Then he leapt forward and seized the animal's trunk. It fell down with a mighty thud. Krishna ripped out the elephant's tusks and with one blow killed both the animal and its mahout. Perspiring, and armed with the bleeding tusks, the brothers entered the arena. The people were at once attracted by the divine glow on their faces. They were thrilled beyond measure that the elephant had been killed. Among themselves, they started talking about the deeds and glories of Balarama and Krishna. Kamsa too, awed by their feat, looked helplessly upon their magnificence, and trembled violently within.

At last the trumpets sounded and the signal was given for the games to start. Chanura, the chief wrestler, approached Krishna and said, with utmost courtesy, "O Krishna and Balarama! Your fame as renowned wrestlers has reached the ears of our king, the great Kamsa. Therefore you have been invited to this wrestling match. We, who are the subjects of the king have to do his bidding and so we request you to match your wrestling skill with ours."

Now Krishna loved this sport, one which he had indulged in so often with the *gopas*, when they were out in the forests with their cows. But he answered, "We, who live in the forests are also the subjects of the King of Bhoja. We too, must do his bidding. But we will wrestle with our equals, that there may be no sense of injustice or foul play."

Chanura replied with great cunning, "Neither you nor your brother is young in experience. You killed an elephant just now, which had the strength of a thousand elephants, as though you were at play. You should not, therefore, hesitate to wrestle with us. Measure your strength with mine and let Balarama tackle Mustika."

The brothers accepted the challenge. Soon, they were locked in fight with the two mighty wrestlers. People grew afraid to watch the supple young bodies of the boys in the grip of the strong-muscled bodies of the seasoned wrestlers, glistening with oil and sweat. They protested that the fight was unequal and cried out to put a stop to it.

Krishna now thought that he had dallied enough. He started hitting his opponent hard with his hands, feet and knees. Chanura could not take the deadly blows and fainted a number of times. With a last spurt, he rose and struck Krishna on the chest

---

* fifty yards.

with the double force of both fists. Krishna received the blow as an elephant receives a flower garland. Then he caught Chanura by the arms and whirling him round and round, dashed him to the ground with such immense force that he did not even have the opportunity to draw his last breath! His body, mangled, lay in the dust, motionless in death. Similarly, Balarama killed Mustika and he too, lay still with streams of blood pouring forth from his mouth. Then he killed Kuta with his fist and Krishna killed Sala with merely a kick of His foot. All the other wrestlers fled from the arena in great terror. Krishna and Balarama danced joyfully as they used to in Vrindavana. They were soon joined by the *gopas* with their tinkling bells making sweet dance music. The trumpets sounded and the crowds rose from their seats crying, "Well done!" "Bravo!" "Bravo!"

Kamsa fumed and seethed with rage. His eyes were red with anger and his body trembled violently with the force of uncontrolled emotions. He ordered the trumpets to be silenced, and shouted, "Drive those two boys out of Mathura. Take away all the possessions of those vile *gopas*. Seize this Nanda and put him in chains. Kill the wicked Vasudeva and my father Ugrasena! Kill!! Kill!!"

But before he could even finish giving his orders, Krishna jumped onto his platform. Kamsa immediately drew forth his sword. But Krishna caught hold of Kamsa by his hair from which the royal crown had tumbled down. He swung him around and threw him down into the arena, still and quite dead. Then he dragged the tyrant all around the arena so that everybody could see him. But in spite of his disgraceful end, Kamsa was rewarded in his last moment with a blissful vision of the Lord in all His divine plendour. For Kamsa, although in a negative way, with constant fear and dread in his heart, had never spent even a single moment without thinking about Him!

Kamsa's eight brothers felt the insult done to their brother. They attacked Krishna and Balarama to avenge Kamsa's death. But they too, were soon overpowered and killed. Kamsa's many wives were inconsolable with grief. But Krishna consoled them and gave them solace.

Krishna and Balarama then hastened to Vasudeva and Devaki and released them from their iron chains and fetters. They prostrated before them and touched their feet in salutation. Krishna also released Ugrasena, who was languishing in a dungeon where he had been thrown by his own son, Kamsa, in his impatience to get his throne.

WITH THE TEACHER

Vasudeva and Devaki embraced their sons from whom they had been so long separated, with great love and tenderness. They kissed them again and again and shed tears of joy. Krishna and Balarama placed the released Ugrasena on the throne. Krishna called back the Yadavas, Vrishnis, Madhus and Dasharhas, who had fled from Mathura in terror of Kamsa and restored to them their rightful properties and homes. The citizens of Mathura now released from the tyranny of Kamsa's reign, lived happily in peace and prosperity.

प्रगृह्य केशेषु चलत् किरीटं
निपात्य रंगोपरि तुंगमंचात् ।
तस्योपरिष्टात् स्वयमब्जनाभः
पपात विश्वाश्रय आत्मतन्त्रः   (स्क. 10 ग. 44 श्लो. 36)

Kicking the crown away, Lord Krishna caught hold of the hair of Kamsa and hauling him down from his throne in a flash jumped on the fallen foe. The Lord is not only the support for the whole universe but he has the whole universe under his perfect control.

Krishna catches Kamsa by the hair and pulls him down

Krishna and Balarama addressed Nanda respectfully and said, "Dear father. You and mother Yasoda shall ever be our real parents, because it was you who looked after us when we were in great danger as infants. We request you now to return to Vraja and comfort our dear ones there. We will soon follow you". Nanda and the *gopas* bade them good-bye and returned to Vraja with heavy hearts.

Vasudeva now felt that it was time for Krishna and Balarama to be initiated into *brahmacharya ashrama*, for them to be invested with the sacred thread and to learn the scriptures from a learned Guru. After the Upanayana ceremony the boys were taken to their teacher, the Rishi Sandeepany. They were required to live in the ashrama of their Guru in strict continence and service to the teacher during the entire period of their studies. The boys were diligent and quick to learn. Under the guidance of Guru Sandeepany, they had mastered the Vedas and the Vedangas, phonetics, grammar, astronomy, logic, the different systems of philosophy and the economic sciences, all within the span of sixty-four days!

Then they approached their Guru and asked him to name his *Guru-dakshina*. The teacher consulted his wife. The extraordinary intelligence of the brothers and the stories of their deeds left no doubt as to their divinity. Rishi Sandeepany said, "We desire no material fees, dear children. But our son was drowned in the sea at Prabhasa. We request you to restore him to us."

Balarama and Krishna set out for the sea-shore. The sea brought forth many precious gifts for them, and honoured and welcomed them. But on being questioned, it denied having swallowed the Rishi's son. Then they went to Yama, the lord of death, and demanded the restoration of their Guru's son. The Guru and the Guru-*patni* were overjoyed to receive their lost son back. Sandeepany bade them farewell with the following blessing, "Go my children to your homes. You have given me the most precious *Guru-dakshina*. May your glory shine wherever you go. May you purify the whole world."

After completing his studies with the Rishi Sandeepany, Krishna went back to his parents in Mathura. But he still had not forgotten his friends in Vraja, nor the happy days he had spent in their company. So one day, he called to him a dear friend of his whose name was Uddhava. He asked him to carry a message of love from him to the people of Vraja. Uddhava was only too pleased to do the Lord's bidding. Krishna himself did not go to Vrindavana, because when an *avatara* is born, it is to fulfil certain purposes in life, and the Lord's mission was yet to start.

AKROORA GOES TO HASTINAPURA

In Mathura, Krishna visited Trivakra, the girl who was now a beautiful young lady, according to his promise. Then, with Balarama and Uddhava, he visited the house of Akroora. Akroora washed the feet of Krishna and received him with great devotion.

"Good people like you are worthy of adoration and worship, Uncle", said Krishna. "Their very presence purifies the world. Please then, proceed to Hastinapura and enquire after the welfare of our cousins, the Pandavas. They are yet young but have lost their father. They are now living with their uncle, King Dhritarashtra. But the blind king is partial to his wicked sons. So please enquire whether the Pandavas and their mother Kunti are happy or not. Then we will see if we can help them."

So Akroora set out on his mission to Hastinapura. There he met king Dhritarashtra and members of the court and the house-hold: the grandsire Bhishma, the wise minister Vidura, the great teacher of archery, Drona, his son Ashwatthama, the eldest of the Kauravas, Duryodhana, and Karna, all the five Pandavas and their mother Kunti. Akroora stayed for some days in Hastinapura. During that time he learnt that the sons of Dhritarashtra were very jealous of their cousins who were more popular with the people because of their intelligence, bravery, skill in the arts and sciences and their great modesty. Many times Dhritarashtra's sons, the wicked Kauravas, tried to do away with the Pandavas, but invariably their plans failed. When the time for Akroora's departure drew near, he requested the old king to be impartial in the treatment of his fatherless nephews. But Dhritarashtra confessed that he was much too attached to his sons for his decisions to be impartial. Akroora, saddened by what he had seen and heard, hastened back to Mathura and gave in detail his report to Krishna.

JARASANDHA AND THE RISE OF DWARAKA

Jarasandha was the king of Magadha. He was the father-in-law of Kamsa, since two of his daughters were married to him. When Kamsa was killed, his wives became widows and sorrowfully returned to their father's house. Jarasandha was terribly angry indeed, and swore to take revenge. He collected an army of twentythree *akshauhinis**. He marched at the head of this huge army, determined to wipe out the Yadava race. Krishna thought for a moment what he should do. Then he decided that he would destroy Jarasandha's army but would spare his life. For, the purpose of an incarnation is to remove the evil and the wicked from the face of the earth. And Krishna thought that if he spared the life of Jarasandha, he would gather his *adharmic* forces again and again and that would give the Lord a chance to do away with as many wicked people as possible.

As Krishna was thinking, there arrived before him two celestial chariots driven by heavenly charioteers. It was fully fitted for the requirements of warfare. The weapons were special and indestructible. Rama and Krishna led a small army of soldiers out of the city gates and rode out in their celestial chariots. They blew their conches and challenged the enemy forces.

Jarasandha said, "Vile Krishna! Killer of your own uncle! I shall not fight you. But I will certainly match my skill and courage with Balarama if he is ready to fight me."

---

* each *akshauhini* consists of 21,870 chariots, just as many elephants, 65610 horses and 1,09,350 foot soldiers.

Krishna said, "A truly brave man never boasts. You are still full of sorrow over your son-in-law's death. So I will not take notice of your words."

Jarasandha's army now surrounded Krishna's army on all sides like the sun and its rays are surrounded by threatening dark, black storm clouds. Women watched from their balconies and house-tops. Soon they lost sight of the brothers and their flags in the midst of the enemy numbers. They trembled with fear at the thought of what would be the fate of Krishna and Balarama against the enemy hordes. Krishna twanged his mighty bow, Sharanga, and let go his arrows with such speed and in such great numbers that they destroyed the enemy in thousands at a time. Men, horses and elephants were scorched by their mighty power. The arrows followed one after another so swiftly that they resembled a giant wheel of fire. Hands were cut off, heads rolled down, legs were severed and bits of shattered weapons and chariots flew into the air. The battle-field was covered by innumerable streams of blood.

Balarama wielded his celestial mace and completed the destruction of Jarasandha's army. Then he attacked Jarasandha who had, by now, lost all his horses, elephants, men and chariots. He was about to bind him with ropes when Krishna stopped him. Jarasandha was set free. So humbled was he that he decided to renounce the world and become an ascetic. But some other kings who were his friends consoled him with worldly wisdom and dissuaded him from doing so. So he returned to Magadha and collected another twenty-three *akshauhinis* and marched to Mathura. Seventeen times was Jarasandha defeated by Krishna and every time he lost his entire army! Yet Jarasandha prepared to lead another twenty-three *akshauhinis* for the eighteenth attempt.

At this time Mathura's might was challenged by a brave hero called Kalayavana. He was followed by an army of thirty *akshauhinis* of *mletchas* (barbarians). Krishna and Balarama discussed the situation. Krishna said, "In a day or two Jarasandha will be upon us with his forces. If, at that time, we are engaged in fighting the Yavana, Jarasandha will capture the city and kill or make prisoners of the citizens. What we must do is build an inaccessible fortress and remove all our people and cattle there. Then by the time we are through with Kalayavana, we will be ready to fight Jarasandha."

This was no sooner said than done. A magnificent fortress ninety-six miles long, rose from the bottom of the sea in the west. Within was a town fashioned with exquisite skill and workmanship. There were buildings with golden towers, and the walls and roofs were decorated with sparkling gems. There were broad roads and lovely gardens and groves with the rarest and most beautiful plants and trees ever seen. Indra presented Krishna with the famous hall for assembly called Sudharma and the Parijata tree whose shade had the unique power of removing hunger, thirst and fatigue. Varuna, the water-god, presented him with the fleetest of horses and Kubera presented him with the eight kinds of wealth of which he was the presiding deity. Then, with his yogic powers, Krishna transferred the entire population of Mathura to the new town which was called Dwarakaa Then Krishna and Balarama emerged from the city gates to fight the Yavana.

MUCHUKUNDA

Now Krishna revealed to Kalayavana, his four-armed form, which he immediately recognised because of the description that Narada had previously given him. Seeing that the Lord was unarmed and on foot, the Yavana also dismounted from his chariot and discarded his weapons. As he approached the Lord, Krishna suddenly turned around and walked away rapidly. The Yavana could not keep pace although the Lord seemed just within reach. After some time, Krishna entered a mountain cave and was closely followed by Kalayavana. However, when the Yavana went into the cave he found no trace of Krishna. On the floor he saw a man who seemed to be sleeping. He thought it was Krishna pretending to be unconscious. With a rude kick be tried to wake him. The sleeping man woke and the moment he looked up, the Yavana was reduced to ashes.

The name of the sleeping man was Muchukunda. The descendant of Ikshvaku, he was a wise and noble king. Once, Indra had become afraid of the asuras and had asked Muchukunda to keep guard over the devas. This the pious king did with such sincere vigilance that the devas asked him to demand any boon save that of liberation which none other than the Lord could give. Muchukunda, tired after his long vigil, asked for the boon of continuous and uninterrupted sleep. This the devas granted him, accompanied by the curse that whosoever woke him up would immediately be reduced to ashes. Thus Muchukunda retired to a mountain cave and promptly went to sleep till he was rudely awakened by the Yavana.

Krishna now revealed himself to Muchukunda, dazzling with youthful beauty. Muchukunda was awed by the divine vision. He felt an upsurge of love for the Resplendent Being and said,"Who are you, who have entered this forest-cave dazzling it with such overpowering glory? Are you the sun-god or the moon-god or the lord of all devas, Indra? I feel that you could be none other than the blessed Vishnu Himself. For who else can equal the glory and beauty of your Being?"

Krishna said, "Dear friend. My names and births have been infinite. This time I have been born as the son of Vasudeva in the Yadava race. Since you are my devotee, I am bound to you by love. Ask what boon you will."

Muchukunda prayed to the Lord, "I was bewildered by your *maya* for many lives, O Lord. But now that I have seen Thee, I desire nothing but infinite love for Thee."

The blessed Lord said, "Muchukunda, your mind is now truly pure. I grant that wherever you go, your mind will ever remain fixed upon Me. With constant meditation and practice of penances, you will attain to My Being."

Muchukunda then retired to Badarikashrama between the peaks of Nara and Narayana in the Himalayas, and practised austerities there. Krishna returned to Mathura and defeated the Yavana's *mletcha* troops. Now Krishna and Rama were carrying the booty to Dwaraka when they were attacked by Jarasandha. The brothers pretended to flee. They climbed a mountain and safely escaped to Dwaraka. Jarasandha pursued them. Nowhere on the mountain could he find them, so he set fire to the whole mountain. Smug and satisfied that he had at last managed to outwit the brothers, Jarasandha returned to Magadha.

RUKMINI HARANAM

In due course, Balarama was married to a beautiful and virtuous princess called Revati. Krishna married Rukmini, the princess of Vidarbha. This is how it came about.

The king of Vidarbha was Bhismaka. He had five sons and one daughter. The eldest son was called Rukmi. He hated Krishna and resolved to give his lovely sister in marriage to Sisupala, the prince of Chedi, who hated Krishna even more. But the king and all the other members of the royal family wanted Rukmini to marry Krishna. Rukmini too, had set her heart on marrying Krishna and was very disturbed to know that Rukmi would never let her do so. But she did not despair. She called to her a trusted Brahmin called Sunanda, and with a message, sent him to the Lord of her heart.

Sunanda was very well received by Krishna. After offering him rest and refreshment, Krishna asked him the purpose of his visit.

Sunanda told Krishna everything that had happened in Vidarbha and said, "I carry for you a message from the princess Rukmini. She has asked me to say that she has set her heart on you, that she would rather die than marry anybody else. She has implored you to save her from the jackal Sisupala who dares to touch the royal share of the lion! The royal princess would have you come to Kundinapura during the days of the marriage festivities, and carry her off in the rakshasa-form-of-marriage*. On that day she will be taken out to the Ambika temple for worship. She has vowed to lay down her life by fasting if she does not see you then. Now Lord, it is all up to you as to what should be done." Saying this Sunanda became silent.

Krishna was the incarnation of Lord Vishnu and Rukmini was the incarnation of His divine Consort, Lakshmi. So it was but natural that they should be life partners on earth too. Krishna laughed heartily when he heard the message of Sunanda, and said, "I too am determined to marry Rukmini and am well aware that it is Rukmi who has caused all this trouble. Tell the princess to take heart. I shall not fail her."

Then Krishna summoned his celestial chariot drawn by four celestial horses and driven by his charioteer, Daruka. In one night be reached Kundinapura.

Kundinapura was a hub of activity. The entire city was swept clean and the streets were sprinkled with water. Garlands of flowers and coloured buntings fluttered and gave it a festive air. Brahmins continuously chanted from the Rik, Sama and Yajur Vedas. They invoked blessings upon the bride and made offerings and oblations to propitiate the unfavourable planets.

---

* According to the rakshasa-system of marriage, rival parties contest for the hand of the bride. She becomes the prize of the victorious party.

116

Bala Bhagavatam

तां राजकन्यां रथमारुरुक्षतीं
जहार कृष्णो द्विषतां समीक्षताम् ।
रथं समारोप्य सुपर्णलक्षणं
राजन्यचक्रं परिभूय माधवः ।   (स्क. 10 घ. 53 स्लो. 56)

Lifting Rukmini, who was herself anxious to get into Krishna's chariot, He placed her in the chariot which had the insignia of the eagle, challenged all the assembled Kings and broke their might, and drove away.
Krishna carries off Rukmini

Sisupala's father, King Damaghosa of Chedi, also performed similar rites and along with his entire army came to Kundinapura. He brought Salva, Jarasandha, Dantavakra, Vidhuratha, Paundraka, and all his other friends along, who were the enemies of Krishna. The bride's father gave them palatial accommodation. Damaghosa brought this vast retinue because he expected Krishna to cause trouble during the marriage festivities. Balarama did not like the idea that Krishna had gone alone, so he too went to Kundinapura with the Yadava army.

In the royal palace, Rukmini was getting extremely anxious as there was no sign yet of either Krishna or the messenger she had sent. It was now the eve of her wedding day and as the hours sped by, she became more and more agitated. She tried hard to strengthen her heart and to restrain her tears. She could not imagine what had happened that Sunanda had not yet come. But in the midst of her sorrow and agitation, she noticed that her left thigh, arm and eyelid throbbed auspiciously. This gave her a faint glimmer of hope. Just then Sunanda arrived and gave her a detailed account of what had happened at Dwaraka. He told her that the Lord was already in the city. Rukmini, in deep gratitude, bowed low before the good Brahmin.

Bhismaka learnt that Krishna and Balarama had arrived in the city. With happiness and love he hastened to welcome them. He presented them with many gifts and received them as highly respected and honoured guests.

Soon, the bridal procession started for the temple of the goddess Ambika. Rukmini, decked in her bridal finery, attended upon by all her maids-in-waiting, stepped into her chariot, which had also been decorated elaborately with gold and gems. The chariot slowly made its way to the temple. The bride, along with her mother and some other elderly ladies of the palace, entered the shrine to offer worship. The trumpets blared forth, the drums sounded and thousands of dancing girls tapped their feet rhythmically and the silvery tinkling of their anklets resounded musically. Inside, Rukmini prayed hard and implored the Mother to grant her request and make Krishna her husband.

The worship over, the bride emerged from the temple and slowly made her way back to the chariot. She looked indeed so beautiful, that the princes who had come from far-off lands to attend the wedding, climbed down from their own vehicles to take a closer look at her. She trembled slightly and prayed that Krishna would appear, while people caught their breath when they beheld her slight, shapely form, and her lovely face framed by dark black hair. Now Rukmini walked even more slowly and played for time. Every now and then she peeped from the corner of her eyes to see if she could catch a glimpse of her Lord. Then, as she was about to enter her chariot, Krishna stepped forward and holding her by the waist, drew her into his own chariot. He seated her on the cushions by his side and before the astounded eyes of Sisupala, Jarasandha and others, he drove away towards Dwaraka. Balarama and the Yadavas followed them. By now Jarasandha and the other kings had regained their senses. As soon as they were able, they gave chase to Krishna and Balarama. The Yadavas used some special weapons and defeated the combined forces of the enemy. But Rukmi was not one to give up and accept defeat so easily. He vowed that he would not return till he had killed

Krishna and recaptured his sister. Krishna, however, soon had Rukmi in his power and was about to cut off his head. But Rukmini fell at his feet and begged him to spare her brother's life. Krishna tied Rukmi with his own scarf and shaved off part of his head and chin. Disagraced as he was, Rukmi did not return to Kundinapura but built a new city for himself where he lived for the rest of his life.

Triumphantly, Krishna carried his bride to Dwaraka, and there with due pomp and ceremony, amid great rejoicing in the city, he married her.

THE JEWEL SYAMANTAKA

There was an honoured citizen in Dwaraka whose name was Satrajit. He was a great devotee of the Sun-god. As a result of his great devotion, the Sun-god was very pleased and presented him with a gem of matchless brilliancy. It was called Syamantaka. This brilliancy became part of whoever wore it, and it produced several hundred kilograms of gold every day!

One day, Satrajit's brother, Prasenajit, wore the jewel and went out hunting. In the forest, he was attacked by a lion who killed him and his horse and took away the jewel. But the lion in its turn was attacked by the bear-chief, Jambavan* who killed him and brought the gem home as a plaything for his little son. Here Satrajit missed his brother and spread a rumour that Krishna had killed him in order to secure the gem for himself. When Krishna heard this accusation, he gathered his men and horses, and in order to prove himself innocent, he set out with them in search of Prasenajit. In the forest they found his remains and also the dead horse and the dead lion. Then, following Jambavan's footprints, they reached his cave in the mountainside. Krishna entered it and grappled with the fierce bear for twenty-eight days. At last Jambavan realised who it was he was fighting with. He prostrated before him and begged his forgiveness for not having recognised him earlier. Krishna explained to him that he wanted the jewel only to prove his innocence. Jambavan gladly gave it to him.

Krishna now returned to Dwaraka and gave the Syamantaka gem back to Satrajit. Satrajit felt truly sorry for having spread such false rumours about Krishna. He caught his feet and asked to be forgiven. And to show his repentance, he presented Krishna with the gem and his beautiful and talented daughter, Satyabhama. Satyabhama became Krishna's wife, but the jewel was returned. "Keep it," said Krishna. "It was a gift to you. But you may give the gold that it produces to the treasury."

At this time, news came to Dwaraka that the Pandavas had all been killed in a fire, as a result of a trap set for them by their wicked cousins, the Kauravas. Krishna and Balarama hurried to Hastinapura to find out the truth about matters.

When the brothers were away, Satrajit was murdered and the gem was taken away from him. Satyabhama rushed to Hastinapura to tell Krishna about it. Krishna and Balarama came back after confirming that the Pandavas were still safe and sound,

---

* Jambavan was a great devotee of the Lord in His previous *avatara* as Rama.

and that the Kauravas' plot had failed. They traced the culprit who had committed the ghastly crime and chased him upto Mithila or Videhapuri. There they killed him but they did not find the Syamantaka on his person. Back in Dwaraka, Krishna found the gem in Akroora's possession. He showed it to Satyabhama which calmed her troubled heart and then returned it to Akroora for safe-keeping.

MURA AND NARAKASURA SLAIN

Mother Earth was again in trouble. Her people were harrassed by a powerful demon called Narakasura. Gods and men both found themselves under his oppression. So Indra approached Krishna for help.

Naraka's capital was a well fortified city and was surrounded by high walls and mountains on all sides. In addition to this, it was surrounded by rings of fire, wind and water. It had been designed by a great asura architect called Mura. The ramparts held self-shooting weapons of all kinds and Mura had laid traps all over which could not be escaped by even the cleverest enemy.

But Krishna overcame all these obstacles. He smashed the ramparts with his mace and his arrows rendered the weapons useless. With his discus he destroyed the three rings of fire, wind and water, and with his sword he slashed the traps. Then he raised his divine conch, Panchajanya, and blew upon it. The sound produced fearful dread in the hearts of the enemies. Mura was, at this time, fast asleep, deep below in the waters. When he heard the oninous sound of the Panchajanya, he rose from the depths, a terrible five-headed monster. He blazed with wrath as he flung his dreadful trident at Krishna. Krishna, however, split the weapon with just two shafts. Enraged and boiling with anger, Mura roared with all his five mouths. The whole earth shook and many felt that the end of the world had come. The Lord sent some more shafts which tore open the monster's five mouths. Then, one by one, Mura's heads rolled down as the divine discus cleared through them. Mura was now dead. One after the other, Krishna killed the asura's seven sons, many other asura generals who opposed him, and then Narakasura himself.

Victorious Krishna entered the palace. There he was welcomed by Mother Earth with hymns and prayers. He found 16,000 young maidens who had been kept captive by Narakasura and many other valuable treasures that the asura had plundered. All these were sent to Dwaraka. Krishna took a Parijata tree for Satyabhama. Back in Dwaraka, he married all the 16,000 fair maidens since they were his great devotees. This was the only way he could protect them since their fathers would not take them back. He built separate palaces for them and multiplied himself so that each one felt that the Lord was her very, very own.

The five-headed monster, Mura, is the ego in each one of us. The five heads are the five-sense organs. The sleeping monster (ego) when it is aroused, plays a death game with the Lord. The Lord, (the divinity in us), ruthlessly uses His divine weapon, the

पांचजन्य ध्वनि श्रुत्वा युगान्ताशनि भीषणम्
मुरः शयान उत्तस्थौ दैत्यः पंचशिरा जलात् ।
(स्क. 10 अ. 39 श्लो. 6)

Hearing the thunderous roar of the Panchajanya-conch of Krishna, the five-headed Mura Asura got up from the depth of the waters.

Krishna slaying Mura

discus,* to destroy the five-headed asura in us. When the ego is thus completely annihilated, the Lord makes a triumphant entry into the palace of our hearts. There, in the holiness of the temple, with prayers and worship, He becomes enshrined as the Supreme King, wedded to all the thoughts in us, the 16,000 captive maidens.

As he was the destroyer of the asura, Mura, Lord Krishna is also known as MURARI.

NARADA SEES KRISHNA'S GLORY

Narada had always been a great devotee of Lord Vishnu. He took great interest in all Krishna's activities on earth. He came to know that Krishna had killed Narakasura and had married the 16,000 maidens that the asura had held captive. "What a marvel!" he thought. "One Krishna and 16,000 wives!" He felt curious to see how Krishna managed to live in peace with all his wives, and how he kept them from quarrelling with each other.

So he came to Dwaraka. Narada could not believe his eyes when he saw the splendour of Dwaraka. He marvelled at the beautiful lay-out of the parks and ponds. In the tranquil waters bloomed lotus flowers of varied hues. There were huge mansions richly decorated, and the roads, market-places and temples were neat and clean. Then he saw the rows and rows of palaces built for Krishna's 16,000 wives. Who can even attempt a description of them? They were the most gorgeous palaces Narada had ever seen. For some time he stood gazing at them in wonder and amazement. Then he made bold to step into one of them.

Here the luxury surpassed his wildest imagination. Canopies made of strings of pearls hung from pillars of coral. The seats and furniture were of ivory and there were luxurious carpets and embroidered curtains. From one of the rooms came the fragrance in incense. Narada entered and saw Krishna resting on a couch. Rukmini was standing nearby and fanning him. Krishna rose to receive the sage. He welcomed him and gave him his own seat. Then he washed Narada's feet and sprinkled the water over his own head as a mark of respect to him. Narada was very pleased indeed and he left the palace offering thanks to the Lord.

Next, he went into another palace. There too, he found Krishna, absorbed in a game with his wife. When he saw Narada, he accorded him a warm welcome. Thus Narada visited every palace and every time he found Krishna engaged in doing a different thing. In one he was playing with his children, in one he was chatting with a consort, in another he was preparing for his prayers. But every time he welcomed Narada with great honour and respect, as though he was meeting him for the first time during the day. Narada was indeed delighted with the Lord's game and, in the end he burst into praise. "O Lord," he said, "Your *maya* is truly wonderful. Who can ever know it fully? Not even Brahma or Shiva. Today, by Your grace, I have seen Your wonderful play in the

* Significantly, the discus, (*chakra*), is called SUDARSHANA – meaning, "auspicious vision."

122

Bala Bhagavatam

कृष्णस्यानन्तवीर्यस्य योगमायामहोदयम् ।
मुहुर्हृष्ट्वा विस्मितो जातकौतुक: (स्क. 10 अ. 69 श्लो. 42)

Narada, seeing the Yoga-maya of Krishna (to be on the same day in 16000 houses at once, revelling in different household duties) was extremely enchanted and again and again marvelled at the infinite glory of the Lord.

Narada visits Krishna after hearing about his 16000 wives

universe. With Your consent, I will now go all over the world and spread Your divine glory."

Krishna said, "My son. Do not be bewildered. My purpose in life is not only to teach the world how to live, but also by practising My *dharma*, to set an example before them."

Narada understood the pregnant suggestion of the Lord's words. Sri Krishna, (as all other *avataras*), manifested in the world not only to teach by words, but to show the world how to live the Divine Life in the home or in the jungle, in the market-place or in the fields. He demonstrated how to live a perfect life in this imperfect world of sorrows and problems, joys and pains.

JARASANDHA VADHAM

One day, Krishna was sitting in his famous assembly hall Sudharama. A Brahmin messenger came and said that he had been sent by over twenty-thousand kings who had been made prisoners by Jarasandha. They, therefore, requested Krishna to come and release them. Just then, Narada too, came with a message that Yudhishtira* was performing a *Rajasuya* sacrifice and that he would be honoured by Krishna's presence at the celebration. Now Krishna found it difficult to decide which duty to attend to first. He turned to Uddhava and asked him for advice.

Uddhava asked all the counsellors what should be done. He then told Krishna that it was his duty to protect those who appealed to him for help and also to attend this great sacrifice. But, he pointed out, a *Rajasuya* sacrifice could not be performed unless all kings had been conquered. As a matter of course, then, Jarasandha would be defeated. As a personal suggestion he added that Jarasandha should be killed by the Pandava prince, Bhima, since he alone had the strength and the stature to equal Jarasandha's. "Let Bhima disguise himself as a Brahmin and ask Jarasandha for single combat," said Uddhava. "He will never refuse a Brahmin anything."

This plan was agreed upon and preparations started immediately. Krishna sent the messenger back to the captive kings with a promise that they would soon be released. Then all arrangements were made for Krishna's visit to Hastinapura. When he arrived at the palace, Krishna was embraced affectionately by the Pandavas. Priests recited from the Vadas. He was welcomed with flower garlands and music. His consorts were also received affectionately by mother Kunti and the Pandavas' wife, Draupadi, with gifts and garlands. Then they were led to their apartments where every comfort had been provided for lovingly, and every requirement attended to lavishly.

One day, Yudhishtira asked Krishna's permission to perform the *Rajasuya*. Krishna readily granted it. He said, "But, Yudhishtira, before you can do so, you have first to subdue all the kings of the earth and only then will you be fit to perform the sacrifice."

---

* The eldest Pandava

सञ्चिन्त्यारिवधोपायं भीमस्यामोघ दर्शनः
दर्शयामास विटपं पाटयन्निव संज्ञया ।   (स्क. 10 अ. 72 श्लो. 43)

Thinking over how best Bhima can kill Jarasandha, Krishna indicated by sign how a plant is split into two.

Bhima poses his problem to Krishna (Jarasandha Vadham)

Yudhishtira was very pleased that the Lord had given His consent. He sent his four brothers to the four corners of the earth. They vanquished all the kings and brought back immense wealth for the treasury. The only king who remained unconquered was Jarasandha. Yudhishtira was very unhappy at this. But Krishna told him of Uddhava's plan, and Yudhishtira decided that no time should be wasted and that the plan should be put into action at once.

And so it happened that three 'Brahmins' – Bhima, Krishna and Arjuna in disguise –set out for Girivraja, the capital of Jarasandha's kingdom. Arriving there, they presented themselves before the king, and as poor Brahmins, begged his favour. Jarasandha was not only a brave warrior, but also a clever and shrewd man. He noticed that their hands bore arrow marks, their bearing was regal and their voices were confident. Besides, one of them looked very familiar. But he thought to himself, "King Bali won fame throughout the three worlds because he granted the request of a Brahmin who was none other than Lord Vishnu Himself in disguise. What is the use of pampering this worthless body, unless a Kshatriya can win fame in this world?" So he turned to the Brahmins and said, "Ask what you will, O Brahmins. I will give you whatever you ask for, even if it be my own head."

Then the 'Brahmins' threw off their disguise. Krishna said, "We are not Brahmins, king. These are two of the Pandavas, Bhima and Arjuna. I am Krishna! Remember me? We have come here to request you for single combat."

Jarasandha laughed and said, "Yes, I remember you. Fools! Of course I will give you fight. But Krishna I will not fight. He ran way to Dwaraka from Mathura. Arjuna is much too small for me and not quite so skilled. Yes, I will fight Bhima, because he is my equal."

He threw a club at Bhima and grabbed one himself. They were indeed equals in fight. For twenty-seven days, all that could be heard was the sound of clubs on human flesh. Each was as brave and as skilled as the other. On the twenty-eighth day, Bhima went to Krishna in a dejected mood. He confessed that he did not know how to defeat Jarasandha. Krishna said, "Jarasandha was born in two parts. Jara, his rakshasi mother, joined him together by her magic." Bhima understood. That day, during the fight, he put his foot on one of Jarasandha's. Before Jarasandha could do anything, he pulled him by the other leg and tore him apart. Bhima had won the fight!

Krishna placed Jarasandha's son, Sahadeva, on the throne. He liberated the twenty-thousand kings, who touched his feet and worshipped him. Krishna said, "Riches and power make a man proud. Know you that the body is mortal and some day has to die. Therefore, do not attach too much importance to it. Keep your minds fixed on Me and rule your kingdoms in peace and happiness."

THE RAJASUYA

Now Yudhishtira was fully qualified to perform the great sacrifice. He sent out invitations to all the Rishis – Vyasa, Bharadwaj, Gautama, Vasishta, Chyavana, Kanva,

तत्पादाववनिज्याप: शिरसा लोक पावनी:

सभार्य: सानुजामात्य: सकुटु बोऽवहन् मुदा । (स्क. 10 अ. 74 श्लो. 27)

Yudhishtira, devotedly washing the feet of the Lord, sprinkled the water upon his own wife's and ministers' heads and they received it with great joy.

Yudhishtira worshipping Krisḥna at the Rajasuya

Maitreya, Viswamitra, Parasara, Jaimini, Garga, Kasyapa, and others; to his relatives–uncle Dhritarashtra, his sons the Kauravas, and the wise Vidura; to his teachers–Bhishma, the grandsire, Dronacharya and Kripacharya; to the many gods and all their consorts, as well as to the numerous ruling kings of the earth.

Elaborate preparations were made for the *Rajasuya*. At last the day dawned and Yudhishtira was initiated as the sacrificer. The ground for the sacrifice was ploughed with a golden plough according to tradition laid down in the Vedas and the vessels used during the ceremony were also of pure gold. The rites were conducted according to the Vedic law. Then the time came for them to choose as to who out of all those who were assembled was to occupy the seat of honour. Many chiefs, chieftains, kings and Rishis were present. After much consultation, Sahadeva, the youngest of the Pandavas, rose and said, "Sri Krishna is the one who deserves respect more than anybody else. He is the essence in all sacrifices. He is the sacrificer as well as the sacrificial fire, *ahuti*, and *mantras*. He is the *atman* in all beings. Therefore, by honouring Him we will be honouring all beings. I suggest that Sri Krishna be shown the highest respect, that He should be worshipped first."

All the good, wise and holy men were very pleased with this suggestion. It was also to the supreme satisfaction of Yudhishtira himself. He rose from his seat and with the utensils of worship, knelt at Krishna's feet. With great devotion and reverence, he washed his feet and sprinkled the water over his own head. Then he sprinkled it over the head of his wife, Draupadi, and his brothers, the four Pandavas. His eyes were full of tears of love as he made offerings of yellow silk and valuable ornaments and gifts. This moment was the climax of the sacrifice. All those who were present felt the sanctity of the occasion. They all stood up and with their palms joined, they saluted Krishna. "*Namo namah!*" (salutations) and "*Jaya! Jaya!*" (victory), they cried.

One among them called Sisupala was a hater of Krishna from his past three lives. He could not bear all this worship of Krishna. Trembling with uncontrollable rage, he shouted in a thundering voice, "It is truly said that Time is the master of everything. You people who are supposed to be wise and old have listened to one who is but a mere child (Sahadeva). Do you not see before you all these great kings and Rishis who have become sinless through their intense *tapas*? Do you not see the great souls before you who have their minds constantly fixed on Brahman? How can you ignore them all and offer the highest worship to this no-good *Gopala* (cowherd)? He is not born of a high caste, nor does his clan possess any tradition or virtue." Thus he went on and on, flinging one abuse after another at Krishna.

Krishna did not react at all to this volley of insults. He uttered not a single word but sat there, calm and cool. His devotees and admirers, however, could not bear to hear Sisupala's outburst. Some covered their ears with their hands and ran out of the hall. The Pandavas and their friends drew swords and rushed upon Sisupala who stood straight and proud and defied them with his shield and sword. But Krishna rose and asked them to be calm. His divine discus came flying through the air and sliced off Sisupala's head. Sisupala's friends and supporters fled in terror. But a wonderful thing indeed happened,

तं विलोक्याच्युतो दुरात् प्रियापर्यकमाश्रितः।
सहसोत्थाय याभ्येत्य दोभ्यीं पर्यग्रहीन्मुदा॥ (स्क.10 अ.80 श्लो.18)

Krishna, who was sitting with Rukmini, seeing from a distance the approaching Brahmin Sudama, got up and ran to embrace him and give him a grand reception.

Krishna runs to meet Sudama

A column of light shot up from Sisupala's body and entered Krishna! All those present beheld the wonder. Like Kamsa, Sisupala had, through continuous hatred, meditated constantly upon the Lord.

The sacrifice then came to an end. Yudhishtira performed the *avabhritha snana**, and all the guests, full of spiritual joy returned home.

DURYODHANA IS INSULTED

Everybody now sang the glory of the *Rajasuya* sacrifice performed by Yudhishtira. Duryodhana burned with jealousy. He could not endure the increasing popularity of the Pandava princes.

One day, Yudhishtira was sitting in his Council Hall. It was in the Hall of Illusions, which the demon Maya had built with great skill and craftsmanship. The proud Duryodhana entered the Hall along with his brothers. His sword was drawn and as he entered, he insulted the gate-keepers and others around. Just then, he saw before him what looked like water. So he lifted up his garments and walked over it only to find that it was actually smooth floor! Another part of the Hall looked like the floor, so Duryodhana stepped on it confidently, only to plunge into a pool of water!

In his insufferable pride and arrogance, Duryodhana had made a complete fool of himself. When they saw how ridiculous he looked, the ladies of the palace along with Bhima and others laughed loud and long. Yudhishtira rebuked them but Duryodhana was angry beyond measure. He lifted himself from the pond and without a word, he left the Hall, his wicked mind bent upon avenging his hurt pride. Yudhishtira was agitated about this. But Krishna said not a word. For slowly, he was working out the destruction of the wicked Duryodhana and his evil supporters.

SUDAMA

Krishna had a poor Brahmin friend called Sudama. The two were class-mates and fellow students in the ashrama of the Rishi Sandeepany. Sudama was very poor. He lived on charity. With the result, not only he but his wife too did not have enough to eat. They lived in a small shack and wore tattered clothes. But Sudama had perfect knowledge of the *atman*, so he was not frustrated. He led a contented life and his wife served him with devotion. Day by day they became thinner and thinner till a time came when the good lady gently reproached her husband and said, "Lord Krishna, master of Lakshmi, the goddess of wealth, is your dear friend. To those who love and worship Him sincerely, He gives His very own self. If you approach Him, will He not give you a few things to keep you out of this misery of starvation?"

Sudama heard but paid no heed. Every now and then his wife would remind him of the glories of the Lord and would ask him to approach Him for help. After many such reminders, Sudama decided to go and pay a visit to Krishna. He thought that if

---

* bathing ceremony which marks the conclusion of a Yagna.

Bala Bhagavatam

निवसतां गुरौ
गुरुवारैश्चोदितानामिश्वनानयने क्वचित् ।
वात वर्षमृतुः ....

(स्क. 10 अ. 80 श्लो. 36)

".......while we were living with our teacher, as wanted by his wife, we went together to the jungle for fuel when, do you remember, we were caught in the rain and storm."

Krishna & Rama in service of their Teacher.

nothing else, he would at least enjoy meeting his old friend again. He asked his wife to give him some gift to take to his friend. She begged a handful of rice from the neighbours, prepared beaten rice out of it, and with this bundled in an old torn piece of cloth, Sudama started off on his journey to Dwaraka.

All along the way he thought of Sri Krishna and felt what a blessing it would be to meet him again. Om Namo Bhagavate Vasudevaya, Om Namo Bhagavate Vasudevaya – sang the great devotee all along his long journey. He passed through the city gates and came before Rukmini's palace. Krishna saw him from afar and ran down the steps to greet him. He was overjoyed to see his old friend again. He embraced him lovingly and led him into the palace. There he made him sit down. He washed his tired feet and gave him refreshment, while Rukmini fanned him. All the servants of the palace wondered why the Lord gave such special treatment to a ragged old Brahmin.

Then Krishna and Sudama talked of their good old days when they were students together with the Rishi Sandeepany. They recalled the happy times they had spent together. Then Krishna said, "Dear friend. I learnt of the hard times you and your good wife have gone through. But he who does his duty with his mind fixed on God knows no grief or misery." Sudama answered that he did not desire anything in the world, because he had had the good fortune of living in his heart with the Lord of the Universe. Then Krishna teasingly asked him if he had brought him any gift. Krishna was well aware of the small packet of beaten rice that Sudama had brought for him, and also knew that he felt shy to give it to him. He said, "Whatever My *bhaktas* give Me with real love, that gift is extremely dear to Me."* Yet Sudama felt shy. So Krishna searched him and from his upper garment drew out the humble gift. He opened the packet and ate a mouthful of the beaten rice. With great appreciation, He said, "This is indeed the tastiest thing I have ever eaten. And you hid it from Me? Truly it will please the three worlds!" And he took another mouthful. Just then Rukmini took the packet away. She said, "Lord! Two mouthfuls are enough. You have eaten up the *tamas* and *rajas* of your devotee with two mouthfuls. Do not eat up the *sattwa* with the third."

That night Sudama slept like a king in Krishna's palace. All through, he had been treated as a most honoured guest. Next morning, he bade his friend an affectionate farewell. Krishna went with him part of the way. His heart overflowing with love, Sudama proceeded on his journey home. He thought, "What if the Lord did not give me any material benefits? So what, if the main purpose of my visit has failed? I am happy in the love of my Lord. He treated me like a god. Perhaps He does not want me to have wealth, lest I should forget Him." Thinking thus he reached home.

But when he got there, lo! What should he see? He could not recognise his poor little hut. So transformed it was! In its stead stood the most magnificent mansion he

---

* पत्रं पुष्पं फलं तोयं यो मे भक्त्या प्रयच्छति ।

तदहं भक्त्युपहृतमश्नामि प्रयतात्मनः

Whoever with devotion offers Me a leaf, a flower, a fruit or water, that I accept – the devout gift of the pure-minded.

had ever seen. There were many gardens and ponds. Servants went about their work. The place was provided with every luxury imaginable. Sudama thought this was a wrong place he had come to, that he had lost his way somewhere. He turned around to go. But a lady dressed in silk and gold came out of the mansion and stopped him. He looked at her and recognised her as his own wife. He knew then that this was Krishna's gift to him. Sudama offered praise to the Lord. Thereafter, he and his wife lived a pure life, avoiding excesses in spite of their wealth. They meditated upon the Lord constantly and ultimately attained the State of His Supreme Being.

SUBHADRA HARANAM

Krishna had a sister called Subhadra. She was a lovely young maiden, virtuous and talented. When she reached the marriageable age, Balarama decided to give her in marriage to Duryodhana. At this time Arjuna was on his travels. In the course, he reached Prabhasa, where he learnt about Subhadra's forthcoming marriage. He determined to marry her himself.

So he arrived at Dwaraka disguised as a *tridandi** sannyasi. He lived on the food that people gave him. One day, Balarama came to know that an ascetic of great merit was in the city. So he sent him an invitation for *bhiksha*. Arjuna went. There he was served by Subhadra. Both Arjuna and Subhadra loved each other. It was fortunate that no one in the palace recognised him. Arjuna then sought out Krishna and told him of his desire to marry his sister. Krishna heartily approved of the proposal. But Balarama would never have listened. So Arjuna decided to carry her off but had to wait for a suitable opportunity to carry out his plan.

One day, Subhadra asked the permission of her parents to go and offer worship at a temple outside the fort. Having secured it, she set out in her chariot along with a number of attendants. Arjuna was waiting for just such an opportunity. He took everybody by surprise and carried away Subhadra. He drove the chariot to Hastinapura fighting and defeating anyone who tried to stop him..

Balarama was very angry at this behaviour of Arjuna's. It was a difficult task to pacify him. But Krishna succeeded in doing so. In his heart of hearts he was extremely pleased that his sister had married Arjuna and not the vile Duryodhana. Balarama and Krishna then sent the couple many elephants, horses and chariots as presents along with many other expensive and valuable gifts.

VRIKASURA

Yudhishtira once asked Krishna a question at the end of the sacrifice. "How is it", he said, "that although Shiva is the Supreme Yogi, ever absorbed in meditation, his followers enjoy great prosperity on earth; and that although Sri Vishnu is the

---

* carrying the triple-staff, a particular order of Sannyasins belonging to Brahmin caste who even after Sannyasa carry out the rituals vigorously.

Lord-of-Wealth*   His followers seem to have absolute dispassion and *vairagya* for worldly objects and worldly enjoyments?"

Krishna replied that Lord Shiva is ever connected with Shakti, which is associated with the manifestation of the *gunas*. Therefore, those who worship him will naturally get the material benefits in this world. On the other hand, Sri Vishnu is beyond even the *gunas*, and to reach Him, therefore, His devotees have to rid themselves of the *gunas*. He said, "Little by little I take away the wealth of him whom I wish to favour. When he is reduced to extreme poverty, he makes new efforts in the material world which get defeated again and again. Ultimately, he seeks the company of My devotees and it is then that I reveal to him My infinite glory."

To explain this point, we are told the following story by the ancient masters.

There was once an awful demon, Vrikasura by name. The whole world was miserable with the burden of his vicious acts. One day, Narada approached him and said that if he wanted to acquire more powers, he should do penance and worship Lord Shiva.

So Vrikasura betook himself to the Himalayas and performed severe penance. Every day he would cut off a piece of his own flesh and offer it in worship to Lord Shiva. Finally a day arrived when he decided to cut off his head as a last offering. He was about to do so when Shiva appeared before him and asked him what boon he desired. Vrikasura, with all the viciousness of his asuric nature, asked the Lord to grant him that the person on whose head he placed his hand should be burnt to ashes. In short, he wanted a "fire-touch". Shiva was bound to grant him the boon. No sooner had he said "*Tathaastu*",** than Vrikasura wanted to test the boon by placing his hand on the very head of Gangadhara himself. At once Shiva realised how dangerous the boon was; but it was too late for regrets. He fled to Vaikuntha and begged Sri Vishnu to help him.

But Vrikasura followed Shiva to Vaikuntha. Lord Narayana disguised Himself as a young brahmachari in the nick of time. He started talking to him. He offered him refreshment and in sweet words asked him the purpose of his visit to Vaikuntha. When Vrikasura told him that he was out to test Shiva's boon, the young brahmachari said, "Do you really believe that Shiva's boon is effective? I do not think so. You see, he was once cursed by Daksha. How can his boon have any effect? I think you can quite safely test the boon on your head." Vrikasura was completely taken in by the brahmachari's sweet words and pleasing manner. And then the Lord's *maya* was working on him too. So trusting the young man's words, he touched his own head with his hand. Lo! In a split second he lay in a dead heap on the floor, as though struck down by lightning. Lord Shiva had been saved by Sri Narayana's Grace, from the tricky situation he had placed himself in, due to his readiness in answering prayers!

* SRIPATHI — husband of Lakshmi, who is the goddess of wealth.

** So be it.

THE AVADHUTA

Krishna's mission on earth was nearing its end. He had, in answer to the prayers of the gods and Mother Earth, killed any number of demons, daityas, and wicked kings. He had played a major part in the great Mahabharata-war in which all the Kauravas and their evil supporters had been killed. The Yadava race had grown proud and arrogant because they felt assured of Krishna's guiding hand in all their undertakings. The time was drawing near for the extinction of the Yadavas. Besides, Brahma, Shiva and the other gods had requested Lord to return to Vaikuntha. Knowing all this, Uddhava touched Krishna's feet with his head and said, "Lord! I am well aware that the end of the Yadus is near, that very soon You will be leaving the earth. I cannot bear to be away from You. Please grant that I may always be with You, that I may never be separated from You."

Krishna then spoke lovingly to Uddhava and gave him teaching on how to live in the world, how to shake off all attachment to worldly things, and how to cultivate supreme devotion to the Lord, in order to attain the blessedness of His Being. This portion in the Bhagavatam is known as the *Uddhava Geeta.* In the course of His teachings, Bhagavan told Uddhava the following meaningful story.

King Yadu once came across a young *Avadhuta**, who seemed to be roaming about aimlessly. Addressing him he said, "Tell me, O learned one, you look as though you had renounced the ego completely. How do you manage to keep such perfect balance in the midst of men who lust after wealth and enjoyment? What is the secret of your inner peace? What enables you to roam the surfaces of the earth, like a child, so free from care?"

The Avadhuta answered, "O noble king, I have roamed freely on the earth and received wisdom from many teachers. They are twenty-four in number. Hear from me about them. They are the earth, air, ether, water, fire, moon, sun; the pigeon, python, sea, moth, elephant; the bee, honey-gatherer, deer, fish; the dancing-girl Pingala and the osprey+ ; the child, the maiden; the arrow-maker, snake, spider and the insect known as *Bhramara-keeta.* Listen then, to the lesson I learnt from each of these teachers*.

"From the EARTH, I have learnt to be tolerant, and to do good only for the sake of others. A wise man should never lose his balance even when he is ill-treated by others. He should be like a tree, which always serves others, no matter how it is treated by the animals and human beings. A man's life should be to this end.

"The AIR, although it carries good and bad odours is never affected by them. Its essential nature is always pure. Similarly, even though moving in the world of good and bad, a man should not be affected by them.

---

*   naked ascetic lost in thoughts of the Lord.
+   the fishing-eagle.
×   Parents must see that children can repeat these 24 teachers in life and what Sri Avadhuta learnt from each of them.

"The *atman* is like the ETHER* (space), present in living and non-living things. It is ever-pure, ever-free. Meditating on this *atman* should a man live and even while in this body he realises his unity with Lord. As the ether remains untouched by clouds driven by the wind, so too should one be, untouched by the constant changes in the world.

"WATER is always cool, comforting, sweet and pure. So too, is a sage. Contact with a sage always purifies a person who seeks his company.

"He is like the FIRE, which is not contaminated by good or bad thrown into it. Fire reduces to ashes even the filthiest thing thrown into it, yet it ever remains pure. So too is a man of God, who destroys the impurities of others, but himself ever remains pure. The Lord assumes many forms in the universe, just as fire assumes the shape of the burning objects. Just as the flames in the fire rise and fall, so too birth and death are but the movements of the body.

"With the revolving of time, one sees changes in the MOON+, but actually the moon itself remains the same. Similarly, birth and death belong to the body, but the *atman* remains the same always, under all conditions.

"The SUN, when reflected in many buckets of water, appears as many suns, but is actually one. So too, the *atman*, when reflected in many individuals, appears as many, but is actually one.

"Once, there lived a PIGEON in a tree with its mate, and its young ones. One day the two pigeons had gone out to look for food. A hunter came and trapped the baby pigeons. When the parents came back and saw what had happened, the mother was so grief-stricken, that she too jumped into the trap. The father was unable to bear the separation, so he too jumped into the trap. And thus the entire family was killed. Similarly, a man comes to grief when he is over-attached to his family and possessions. He loses his reason and self-control. Born as a human being, one should strive to reach Brahman, for all our attachments to the world of sense objects drag us down.

"A PYTHON is content with what food comes its way. So too, a wise man is happy with the food he gets, whether it is tasty or badly cooked. He does not struggle to keep his body well-fed, because his mind is constantly engaged in the contemplation of the Lord.

"When the OCEAN is quiet, it is calm and placid. So too is a wise man, ever tranquil in his Knowledge. Just as the ocean never overflows its boundaries, so too the man of enlightenment never transgresses his own tranquillity.

"A MOTH is indifferent to its great danger when it is attracted by the flame. Ultimately it gets burnt by it. He who does not have sufficient self-control, and is easily attracted by the sense-objects of pleasure, he, like the moth, ultimately gets destroyed by them, due to his over-indulgence.

---

* *Akasa.*   + Crescent, or half or full moon.

Like an ELEPHANT is caught in a trap by the touch of the she-elephant, so too a man with lust is caught. Look not at anyone with lustful eyes.

"The BEE gathers honey from all flowers. A wise man learns from all sages and scriptures, and sees only the good in them.

"The HONEY-GATHERER steals honey from the bee-hive. But the bees neither enjoy the honey themselves nor do they let another do so. Be not greedy and miserly like the honey-bees.

"A DEER is attracted by sweet sounds and so is easily caught in a snare. A man should take warning from this and not be drawn by sounds which just sound sweet.

"A FISH, because it is greedy is caught by the bait on the hook. He who has no control over his sense of taste meets with a similar end. The organ of taste is the most difficult to control. Once it is controlled, it is easy to control all the other organs.

"Once upon a time there lived a dancing girl called PINGALA. One evening, as usual, she stood at her door, hoping that she would catch some rich man who would reward her with untold wealth for her services. Soon it was night-fall and yet no one came. Suddenly she realised her folly. She said to herself, "How foolish I have been! I have waited for the favours of mere men, when I could have the eternal favour of God. Forgetting the immense wealth of His love, I have sought the wealth of others. The Lord is the friend of all. He has shown me His grace by making me realise this. Truly, I have been foolish, but no more." Pingala soon gave up all her worldly pleasures and composed her mind in meditation upon the Lord. Hope for worldly enjoyments only brings misery. When this hope is renounced, one gains the highest bliss.

"Once an OSPREY was carrying a fish in its beak. It was pursued and attacked by a number of stronger birds, who tormented him. The moment he dropped the fish, they stopped troubling him. Similarly, when a man is attached to an object, it brings him misery. But the moment he leaves it, he enjoys peace and calm.

"I am like a CHILD, carefree and happy, because I have no attachments. Praise and blame are alike to me. My only Play-mate is my Lord. The difference is, the child is happy through ignorance. The wise man is happy in Knowledge which has taken him beyond the *gunas*.

"I once learnt a lesson from a MAIDEN. It so happened that a young man and his party came to see her to seek her hand in marriage. Before the food could be prepared, the rice had to be husked. But the girl did not want the party to know that she had to do this task herself. But as she husked the rice, her bracelets made plenty of noise. She felt sure that they would come to know what she was doing. So she removed all her bracelets, leaving two on each arm. But even these made a tinkling sound. So she removed two more bracelets leaving only one on each arm. From then on, her work was smooth and noiseless. From this maiden I have learnt there is always a lot of noise and quarrelling where many people live together. Even where there are two people, there is small talk and gossip. Therefore, it is best to be solitary and alone. One should then control the scattered thoughts of the mind and fix it in meditation upon the Lord.

"The attention should be fixed upon the Lord with as great a concentration as the ARROW-MAKER'S, who is not conscious of anything else when he is fashioning an arrow.

"A SNAKE enters and lives in a hole which has been made by others. It is not particular about where it sleeps. A sage seeks out caves. What home can he be attached to? He is silent and modest and only speaks words which are beneficial to others.

"Just as the SPIDER spins out the thread from its own mouth, weaves it into a web, plays with it and then withdraws it into itself, so too, the Lord, brings out the the world from Himself, plays with it and then withdraws it into Himself. In essence His nature is ever Blissful, Unchangeable and full of Knowledge.

"The larva (*Keeta*) by constantly thinking of the BHRAMARA becomes the *Bhramara*. Similarly a man becomes that which he constantly thinks about.

"All this I have learnt from my twenty-four teachers. And my own BODY has taught me that it is the most impermanent thing in the world. It is subject to birth and death. Therefore, I have learnt that I am not the body and that, being only the "dweller" in the body, I am separate from it. Man pampers this body, acquires wealth and enjoyments for its sake, but it finally withers and dies away, leaving everything behind.

"Of all God's creatures, man alone has the equipments to realise his oneness with God. He alone is a rare and privileged incarnation. Therefore, instead of wasting time in pursuit of worldly enjoyment he must employ his time in seeking God.

"Truth can be learnt from many teachers – for truth is one, but sages call it by different names."*

YADUKULA SAMHAR

Thus, and in many other words the Lord taught Uddhava. He advised him to go to Badari, and shaking off all attachments, there to plunge himself in deep meditation that he may become one with the Lord Himself.

The end of the Yadus was near. Krishna saw that they had all taken large draughts of an intoxicating drink. In their drunkenness, they caught hold of any weapon they could lay their hands on and killed each other indiscriminately. Instead of lessening, this fury grew more and more. Soon, all the Yadus had killed each other, like a fire consumes a forest, leaving not a single tree alive.

---

* एकं सद् विप्रा: बहुधा वदन्ति
  Rik – Veda Mantra

The Essence of Wisdom

श्री शुक :–

अहं ब्रह्म परं धाम ब्रह्माहं परमं पदम्
एवं समीक्षन्नात्मानमात्मन्याधाय निष्कले ।
दशन्तं तक्षकं पादे लेलिहानं विषानन.
न द्रक्ष्यसि शरीरं च विश्वं च पृथगात्मनः ॥

(स्क. 12 अ. 5 श्लो. 11–12)

Last words of Suka :

"I am Brahman,
the Supreme Resort !
Brahman am I,
the Supreme State !" ......
thus re-cognise yourself
in your own Self.
Then you shall not
see either your body,
or this world,
or the terrible Takshaka
who is coming
near you
with his tongue out
to bite you.

Balarama had already gone to the sea-shore. There he sat, his body locked in *yoga asana*, his mind in deep meditation. Krishna too, sat under a peepul tree. He assumed the form of Sri Narayana, four-armed, bright and shining. He placed his left foot on his right thigh and leaned back against the tree-trunk. A hunter called Jara mistook the tender foot of the Lord to be the mouth of a deer, and shot an arrow at it. Jara was full of sorrow when he realized what he had done. He fell at Krishna's feet and begged of him, his pardon. Krishna told him, "Do not be afraid, Jara. You have only carried out My own will. You will go to heaven with My blessings."

LORD LEAVES FOR THE SUPREME ABODE

Brahma, Shiva, Parvati, the Parjapatis, siddhas, gandharvas, apsaras, vidyadharas and the scores of other celestial beings now all gathered to witness the divine event of the Lord's return to Vaikuntha. Krishna's serene gaze dwelt upon them for a while. Then he closed his eyes, meditated upon his own Self, and in that very same form, he ascended to Vaikuntha. The celestials beat their drums, played their instruments and blew their conches, for there was much joy as they sang of Sri Narayana's divine glory.

PARIKSHIT MOKSHA

This entire story of the Lord's play in the world was related by the great sage, Suka, to King Parikshit, remember? Now when the story came to a close, Parikshit touched the feet of the divine Rishi and with bowed head and folded hands, said, "Great has been my fortune in listening to the wonderful stories of the Lord. The time for my end has now come. My mind is free from the fear of the serpent and of death. Permit me now to fix my mind on the divine glory of Sri Vishnu, and thus to give up this body in contemplation of Him."

Sri Sukadeva blessed the king and left along with the other Rishis and sages who had gathered. Parikshit was now quite alone. He spread the *kusa* grass evenly and sat on it, motionless, his mind composed in steady meditation. Takshaka, the serpent deputed to kill the king, approached him in the form of a Brahmin. He bit the king viciously and his deadly venom immediately reduced Parikshit's body to ashes. The great king had given up his body while meditating upon the Blissful Form of Lord Vishnu! The gandharvas and apsaras and other celestial beings rained flowers on his mortal remains. The three worlds sang the praises of the righteous king and mourned his loss in the world. But Parikshit had forever merged with the Lord and attained His Supreme Being.

THE VISION OF MARKANDEYA

There once lived a great Rishi called Markandeya. He was initiated into *brahmacharya ashrama* by his father. He was an ascetic of supreme merit. He lived a strict life of penance and performed most rigorous *tapas*. He wore his hair matted and dressed in the bark of trees.

He spent many, many long years in meditation.	Seeing the steadiness of his contemplation, Indra became nervous. He sent the most beautiful and accomplished apsaras to distract the sage's attention. They sang and danced before him, but not once did Markandeya's mind waver. Sri Narayana was extremely pleased with the intensity of his *tapas*. He appeared before him and said, "I am greatly pleased by your devotion to Me. Ask for any boon that you will." Markandeya worshipped the Lord and said, "Lord, I wish to be shown the play of Your divine *maya* in the Universe, which tricks men into seeing different forms and beings where, actually, only You exist." The Lord blessed Markandeya and returned.

One evening, it so happened that the Rishi was engaged in worship on the banks of the Pushpabhadra river. Suddenly, a gust of wind came up and within moments it turned into a raging storm. There were flashes of lightning and the rivers rose in angry flood. Soon there was water everywhere. All life on earth was wiped out. The rising sheets of water even drowned the sky and the stars! Only Markandeya found himself borne aloft by the waters of the flood, along with some of the fierce animals belonging to the ocean. He was in utter despair. He was cold and hungry and there was darkness all around. At other moments he found himself in joyous ecstasy and knew not what to make of his strange experiences.

As the floods continued to toss him up and down, he saw, on one patch of the ocean, a small patch of light. Then he saw a small island lifted up. On the island was a *vata** tree. On one of the leaves of the tree he saw a divine Baby, resting joyfully. It had a dark complexion and was the source of the light that Markandeya saw. The Baby had a beautiful face, fresh and glowing. The sides of the leaf had turned up like a basket. The divine Baby smiled at Markandeya and lifting His foot, began to suck His big toe⁺. Markandeya was thrilled beyond measure on beholding the unique Vision. He stepped closer to the Baby and was surprised to find himself being sucked in by the Baby's breath. There inside he was amazed to find not only himself but also his ashrama, and the river Pushpabhadra. Next moment he was exhaled by the Child, and he found himself again out on the flood. And the Child smiled at him happily. Markandeya made to hold the Child in his arms and embrace it. But suddenly, It disappeared and with It disappeared the entire flood, the little island and the banyan tree. Markandeya was once again standing in front of his ashrama on the banks of the Pushpabhadra, offering worship to the Lord.

The several million years of the *pralaya* passed as a few minutes in the Vision of Markandeya. In response to his prayer, the Lord had made him a witness of His divine

---

* banyan

> करार विन्देन पदारविन्दम्
> मुखारविन्दम् विनिवेशयन्तम् ।
> वटस्य पत्रस्य पुटे शयानं
> बाल मुकुन्दं, मनसा स्मरामि ॥

⁺ Holding His feet with His hands, the toe inserted in His mouth, lying in a cradle - of - Bannyan leaf—that Beauty–child–divine, I meditate upon.

maya, and had Himself appeared to him as the lovely Baby on the angry flood waters of the great deluge. Time itself is our imagination only.

THE GLORY OF HARI NAMA

When Krishna departed from this earth, with him departed truth, piety, righteousness, fortitude and all glory. The age of *Kali* began. Even so, the very utterance of the Lord's holy name is purifying and elevating.

HARE RAMA HARE RAMA, RAMA RAMA HARE HARE
HARE KRISHNA HARE KRISHNA, KRISHNA KRISHNA HARE HARE

HARE RAMA HARE RAMA, RAMA RAMA HARE HARE
HARE KRISHNA HARE KRISHNA, KRISHNA KRISHNA HARE HARE

HARE RAMA HARE RAMA, RAMA RAMA HARE HARE
HARE KRISHNA HARE KRISHNA, KRISHNA KRISHNA HARE HARE

HARE RAMA HARE RAMA, RAMA RAMA HARE HARE
HARE KRISHNA HARE KRISHNA, KRISHNA KRISHNA HARE HARE

Constant meditation upon His Lotus Feet drives away all sorrows and evils. It purifies the heart; it increases love for Him, who is the Lord of Love and Life; it brings to the devotee supreme wisdom.

Blessed indeed are those who have Him ever enshrined in the sacred temples of their hearts.

Let us then, constantly remember the divine Flute-Bearer of Vrindavana, and dedicating all our actions to Him, gain spiritual enlightenment and at-one-ment with Him.

यदा तदा यथा तथा तथैव कृष्णसत्कथा ।
मया सदैव गीयतां तथा कृपा विधीयताम् ॥

Wherever I am, in whichever state, bless my Lord, that I may always sing the praise of Thy Sacred Stories.

OM NAMO BHAGAVATE VASUDEVAYA
OM NAMO BHAGAVATE VASUDEVAYA
OM NAMO BHAGAVATE VASUDEVAYA

॥ हरि ॐ तत्सत् ॥